RED COUCH IN THE SKY

JUDITH NICOL

Red Couch in the Sky

Judith Nicol

Copyright © 2021

ISBN: 978-1-9163977-0-5

Published by Judith Nicol in conjunction with Writersworld. This book is produced entirely in the UK, is available to order from most book shops in the United Kingdom and is globally available via UK-based Internet book retailers and www.amazon.com.

Copy edited by Ian Large

Cover design by Jag Lall

Bust Mosaic Statue photograph by Judith Nicol

Border and background images from Pixabay

www.writersworld.co.uk

WRITERSWORLD
2 Bear Close Flats
Bear Close
Woodstock
Oxfordshire
OX20 1JX
United Kingdom

☎ 01993 812500
☎ +44 1993 812500

The text pages of this book are produced via an independent certification process that ensures the trees from which the paper is produced come from well managed sources that exclude the risk of using illegally logged timber while leaving options to use post-consumer recycled paper as well.

For my family.

Most especially for Stephen and
for Matt, Josh and Tim.

And for my friends. Thank you all.
I have been so blessed to have you in my life.

CONTENTS

CHAPTER 1

Asparagus (*Asparagus officinalis*)

2020

March 20th

Bushby House garden

I'm in a right tizzy. After years of change and stress, I was in a good place, before the announcement that is. I look and feel great. People stop to admire me, and I have to say, it's nothing less than I deserve, after years of neglect. And now all this Covid lark is set to disrupt everything. Just my luck. Spring is round the corner, the busiest and most stressful time of the year, and on top of that, a full national lockdown. What about those people who come every week to mow the grass? Does that count as essential work? Everything is going to get so unsightly again.

If only it were November when most of me becomes dormant. How lovely to go to sleep and then re-emerge after the cold winter, when hopefully the virus will be a thing of the past. The prospect of a long spring and summer, nose to the grindstone with all the usual distractions and entertainment kiboshed by this damned lockdown is depressing. No holiday visitors coming into the village to stop and take photos of me. No coast-to-coast cyclists to look out for as they come zooming down the hill opposite and turn sharp left through the village. No school children in the playground over the road to listen to. No early morning dippers going to the outdoor swimming pool. It's all going to be so tedious.

Alice (the ghost who inhabits the mosaic torso in the herbaceous border)

Ee by gum. Gi' o'er bein' so nesh. Yer a reight misery. Always feelin' sorry fer thissen. Always lookin' fer downside. Yer should mek most o' things. Look around yer. And think on, those two

3

won't bi takin' off on 'oliday any time soon. So, more time fer fussin' o'er thee. Ah'm lookin' forward t' lockdown. T' peace and quiet. So calm thissen down. Sun's shinin' an' spring's in air. Best season o' year. Tek a chill pill and enjoy thissen. Reight, ah'm off. Time fer mah sun salutation. Tarra.

Bushby House garden

The new owners moved into the house about six years ago and brought Alice. I didn't know her as Alice then. It turned out she was the late grandma of the lady of the house. We've had other ghosts over the years, but normally they prefer indoors. At first, that Yorkshire twang of hers was darn irritating, and she used to spend the days wandering around. She said she was looking for the perfect resting place. Since she found her preferred spot in the middle of the herbaceous border, she's become all Zen like. All that new age meditation and chanting, what a load of codswallop. And now I'm under pressure to join in. She says I'm too uptight.

When I found out a couple of townies had bought this place, my heart sank. From down south, near Manchester. 'What would they know about the countryside?' I imagined they probably had one of those neat little town gardens, or even an astroturf lawn.

But Alice said green fingers were in the genes. She told me about the huge allotment her husband used to keep behind their bungalow in Cleethorpes. Got him out from under her feet. They lived off it. Hardly spent anything on food, except for the odd scrag end of lamb or occasional bit of fish from the market. I felt sorry for her when she explained how tired of the world she had become. Bringing up two sons during the war years and putting

4

up with her battle-axe of a mother-in-law had worn her down, and she took to resting on the couch all day. Glass half empty, she just wanted peace and quiet, and nothing more to do with anyone. She knew that behind her back the family made fun of her constant state of misery. But by the time she died, she didn't care. How sad. She's such a different being since she came here. In fact, I find her cheerfulness rather irritating.

When they first moved in, they had builders trampling through me for months, flattening everything in their wake. You know what builders are like, no respect for anything. And then it rained like it can do in Cumbria, and I was reduced to a right muddy mess. And to think, in my heyday, I was a fine Victorian specimen. Everyone was waxing lyrical about how the house had been brought back to life, how the village looked so much better without that dilapidated eyesore in the middle of it. But what about me? I was trashed.

After the work was finished and they moved in, they had a big party for everyone who had worked on the house. A good do apparently. All very well for them inside, a glass of something in their hand and everything freshly painted, underfloor heating and all that. I realise now that my carping stopped me having to think about what plans they might have for me. And truth be told, I had got used to doing my own thing without anybody interfering. Shrubs had been left unpruned for ten years or more and had grown into small trees. Seedlings had chosen their perfect spots on the gravel path or in the flower beds and grown strong and tall, without fear of being pulled up. The climbing roses and clematis rambled unrestrained over uncut hedges. Weeds filled any remaining spaces.

Asparagus (*Asparagus officinalis*)

I felt ashamed of my appearance, but it was also very liberating, not having to bother how I looked. And after a while, I just got used to it. The thing that did get me down were the bloody rabbits, hundreds of them, running rampant all over the place. My lawn was in a right old state before, but now there were huge holes everywhere in it. That hurt my pride. Locals used to come in with air rifles and shoot them for target practice. It was like they and the rabbits were in cahoots, taking advantage of my sorry state, almost poking fun at me. I think that's why Alice and I struck up such a friendship. We understood where each other had come from.

About three months after the house was finished, I saw the mini digger arriving and braced myself. 'This is not going to be pretty, and it's going to hurt,' I thought. The bucket went down, the gearstick was put into forward and the clearing began. The noise of the grinding against the stubborn old roots was atrocious. The vibrations went to my very core. In the blink of an eye, gone was the dense prickly undergrowth and the thick trunks and stems of the huge shrubs. I looked even more dreadful than before. Then they asked that bloke with the wonky leg to come and dig over the borders.

That was a job and a half. He thought double digging would get rid of all those perennial weeds. 'Ha! I'll show him,' I thought. 'And does the lady of the house know what a job it is to plant and then cultivate such a large herbaceous border?' I was hoping for Delphiniums, Anemone and Verbena. Maybe even Agapanthus. All very classy. Showstoppers. But before the ground cover gets established, the weeds will have a field day, seeding themselves wherever there is bare earth, and if she doesn't pull them up, it will look a right mess. We don't want to finish up the garden equivalent of 'all fur coat and no knickers'. Do they realise this place was once inhabited by admirals and colonels and even a Director General of Bermuda?

Alice told me I was being a drama queen, as only she can, 'Yer getting' thissen all mithered and in a reight ol' state, all fer note. Anyroad, she's doin' a college course, and she knows all 'em fancy long names fer things. 'Er grandad would bi reight proud, so 'ee would. It'll bi champion, mark mah words. Now calm thissen. How 'bout two o' us do some yogic breathin'?'

Then they cleared the gravel paths down the middle and chopped back the unwieldy yew bushes. God, they looked awful, full of holes and bare stems. I felt like I'd been to the barbers and had a Number One all over. It would be years before it looked anything like a proper hedge again. And then they set about the old ash tree beyond the yew hedge. That young tree surgeon with the curly hair and beard said it was unstable and might come down in a storm. I heard a few villagers tutting about 'letting it be'. But down it came with a heart-breaking thump. They left the stump and made it into some trendy 'bug hotel'. Call me old fashioned, but insects have been doing their own thing for decades around here, without the need for fancy accommodation. Must have been learning about it on that course of hers.

Next was a big pergola down the central pathway. I thought it was a bit 'House and Garden magazine' to be honest. And it would be years before those wisterias come into flower. The lawn was re-laid, and more ground under the big old yew tree cleared and returfed. The new sandstone patio outside the

7

sitting room was completed. It's huge. Big enough to have a square dance on it.

After they first moved in, the lady of the house used to disappear every week. Dressed in her work clothes and carrying an overnight bag and computer case, she caught a train to London, usually before daybreak in the winter. The car crunched its way down the drive long before the first horses of the day passed by. Then, a couple of days later, the car came back again, and she used to get out, stretch her arms up to the sky and breathe in the air. If it were still light, she would reappear minutes later, changed into her dog walking clothes. She needed to be in the fresh air. After a few years the journeys stopped, and since then she has spent all her time here. I'd call it a bit of a win win. Good for her and I've definitely benefited from the attention.

I couldn't fault them for their efforts. And as I got to know them, I decided they weren't as bad as I'd feared. Well at least they were going to live here. There are so many second homes in the village, and that's no good for the post office or the pub or the school. After the locals got used to them, they would lean over the newly laid hedge and chat if they saw them working in the garden. Sussing out the incomers. They'll never be one of us, most thought. Others just gawped without passing the time of day.

A few years on, I got to like my new look, sort of cottagey and informal but classy at the same time. After the long winter sleep, it was good to look forward to any new plants that had been added the previous autumn. Then she got herself a greenhouse. Painted it that trendy Farrow & Ball blue colour. White was traditional in my day, but it doesn't look too bad actually. Thinks she's Felicity Kendal off The Good Life, with her gardening apron, dungarees, and wellingtons. Gosh, I'm showing my age now. That's a blast from the past. Mind you, I rather go for her.

About this time of year, she fills all the shelves of the greenhouse with seed trays full of courgettes, beans and sweet peas. Once they have germinated and grown strong, she plants them out in the raised beds made from old sleepers found in the coach house garden. She used to be on the 'let's make it totally organic bandwagon' until everything got eaten by the slugs. Then there was the time she planted the seedlings outside, and the fat pigeon was watching her intently from the tree the other side of the greenhouse. As soon as she went back into the house, he swooped down and had his breakfast lunch and dinner all in one easy picking. But she refused to be beaten, got some decent netting, and third time lucky we got some worthwhile produce.

Last summer, I began to notice that every Friday she would appear with her secateurs to harvest the sweet peas in the vegetable patch. Why she wanted to mix flowers and vegetables was beyond me, but they did brighten things up. She would come out with her cup of coffee and sit on the chair next to the greenhouse in the morning sun. She loved the solitude and peace. It was nice to watch her sitting there, completely happy in her own company. Content. The washing was drying on the whirly line next to the raised beds. Not quite as it used to be. The maids used to scrub the laundry in the dark, low-ceilinged servants' quarters, then hang it on long washing lines, out of view.

She used to take the bunches of sweet peas across the drive

to the two holiday houses, for the visitors to enjoy. They were converted from derelict outbuildings and finished about two years ago. This time the builders were given strict instructions not to trample me to death. Now guests come and go every Friday and Saturday on changeover days. Most are friendly enough, pleased to be out of the smoke. They peer over the wall next to the driveway to get a good look at me. Truth be told, I have got used to their admiring glances. Billy, our dog, is delighted with all the people coming and going and sniffs them contentedly. Useless guard dog mind you, he just lies on the lawn, his ears twitching as things go by. Yes, he too is going to miss all the spring and summer holiday action this year.

And guess what, we even have an asparagus bed now. *Asparagus officinalis* is its Sunday name. One of their farming friends gives them some well-rotted compost to get it going every year. How the Director General of Bermuda would have approved. Proper traditional kitchen garden. And they've planted hundreds of trees in the meadow, to help stop it flooding. The locals are happy it's not going to be sold to a housing developer. We've now got more native hedges than you can shake a stick at, and even that yew hedge they butchered is growing back nicely. The guy with the wonky leg and his wife cut them back at the end of the season and they look just the ticket, neat as anything for the winter.

About four years ago, she also started to make these abstract mosaic sculptures. They are my centrepieces. Some people in the village stop and scratch their heads when they see them. I have grown to like them. They're slightly bonkers, but I love the colours and textures, and they're made using upcycled *china. If she carries on making them and doesn't sell any, it's going to get pretty crowded around here. First, we got Venus, the female torso in the herbaceous border. That's where Alice, her grandma, decided to settle. Think she likes the sparkle of the mirror bits in the sunshine. She loves it here. Says nobody bothers her, but she can see everything from her raised position in the middle of the Salvias and the Astrantias and watch over her granddaughter. She was always her favourite.*

I'm a creature of habit and I don't like change. But being right in the centre of the village has been a constant for me. Nothing happens around here that I don't know about. The horses go past three or four times a day, backwards and forwards between the racing stables and the forest gallop. What a racket. I first hear hooves clip clopping up the road just after sunrise. The jockeys are all very cheery, considering the time of day. Not quite so smiley on a dark rainy morning it must be said. If she is in the garden when they pass later in the morning, they shout over the hedge, 'Morning' or 'Nice garden'. When it's sunny and warm, the one at the front who's in charge smiles, 'Another day in paradise.' She raises her coffee cup to him and nods in agreement.

All year round, the pub the other side of the village green provides me with hours of entertainment. I like it best in the summer months when dozens of coast-to-coast cyclists stop there around late afternoon. Bikes everywhere. Sweaty competitive men in Lycra. I watch them drinking their pints, tops unzipped to reveal more flesh than I care to see. You won't be laughing when you get back on your bikes, I think to myself.

And what sights for sore eyes there are in the car park as the early morning swimmers go towards the open-air pool for their pre-breakfast dips. I believe they call them lidos nowadays. She goes too. Loves it she does, though she's so bleary-eyed as she sets off with her backpack, I swear she doesn't fully wake up until she jumps into the water. Then there's the lady in the white bath robe and flipflops, goodness knows I thought we had another ghost the first time she appeared. Others cycle there, their swimming bags swinging on the handlebars. Even when the weather turns wet, they're all down there every morning, as regular as clockwork. It's an important part of their social life. After it closes for the season, some of them swim in the lake all through the winter. Bonkers. I'm getting ready for my long sleep by then.

Sometimes, she brings her friends back after the morning swim for coffee or breakfast. They all sit outside at the big table on the patio, 'That was so lovely. Aren't we lucky?' They plan their so-called 'gin and swim' holidays midst much laughing and joking. Last year it was in Majorca. Seems there's a story or two, more gin than swim, but what happens on tour, stays on tour. I've also heard there's some skinny dipping goes on at the pool. Whatever next?

So, you can see why I was so miserable about the prospect of lockdown. Just wouldn't be the same without all of this activity. But, far from being overly quiet, it has seen lots of unexpected comings and goings. Their three grown-up kids have all come home. And two girlfriends as well. A right little commune. It's just like during the Second World War when this place became a school for evacuees from down south. To begin with, it threw Alice and me. We had got used to our little routines. But soon it became the new normal. They all have their routines too. A run or a cycle ride in the morning, then working at their laptops during the day. In the evenings, they take Billy for a walk or go to the lake for a swim. Sometimes they find a sunny spot and read. The weather has been so warm ever since the first day of lockdown.

I don't know what it is about this family and gin, but even the field behind me has been renamed. The first time I heard them talking about the 'gin meadow', I wondered what on earth they were on about. Whatever next? At weekends, they all walk down there and gather round the big table in the early evening. It still gets the sun long after I am in shade. The father brings his rucksack full of gin, cans of Fever Tree tonic (her favourite) and Thermos flask full of ice. Everyone is equipped with their own glass. They all sit around like they're at some kind of festival. They even bring that ghetto blaster thing with them. The dog messes around in what remains of the stream or sits under the table, waiting for the odd crisp or biscuit. Don't tell anyone, but it's the most fun I've had in years. Always someone around. I do love people watching. Alice was right. Every cloud has a silver lining.

I watch the lads trying to bottle the homemade beer. All the gear, no idea. That's another lockdown first. Great big plastic containers of brown liquid appear on the patio from time to time and at least three of them crowd round scratching their heads, holding lots of tubes. One of them lies on the patio floor, trying to encourage the liquid into the pipe until it all comes out in a great big gush and he gets covered in the stuff. There's a lot of laughing and leg pulling. I'm quite sorry when it's all been done.

Asparagus (*Asparagus officinalis*)

They sit outside until nearly midnight in the long June evenings, taking in the views and watching the bats flying above them. They don't need to make a fire, it's still so warm. The birds are noisier this year on account of fewer cars on the road and planes in the sky. Alice and I are loving it. We listen out for the swallows calling to each other and imagine what they might be saying. And you would not believe the number of red squirrels this year.

One of the boys has a birthday in the middle of June. He's been a bit grumpy because he would rather be with his mates. I'm rather looking forward to it. I like a good bash. First, there's a table tennis competition on the back patio. That's fun to watch, until the inevitable bat slamming when someone doesn't like losing. They're so competitive those lads. The Middle Eastern feast must have taken all day to prepare. It looks fantastic. Oval platters of brightly coloured salads, dishes of couscous and a conical earthenware tagine all laid out on the big table next to the house.

Fresh flowers she cut this morning and candles and tealights. And some posh wine, though I did hear the father complaining, 'I don't know why I bothered to buy some really nice stuff because it all gets necked down so fast.' When they have finished eating, they all sit back and start to play games. Birthday boy is getting some ribbing, with everyone acting out and guessing his most memorable moments. He's obviously got a bit of history, but he sits there and takes it. Occasionally he reminds his brothers of some things they too would rather forget. No one escapes the family banter. And then the three-tier chocolate sponge cake arrives with sparklers on it and they all sing 'Happy Birthday'. It's the early hours of the morning before they clear the table and move indoors.

Alice (the ghost who inhabits the mosaic torso in the herbaceous border)

They know 'ow to enjoy the'selves, reight enough. The way them lads backchat their mam and dad. They'd 'ave got a good clip round ear in mah day. But they're good'uns and she ne'er banked on gettin' 'em all back after they fled nest. When they wor little 'uns and she 'ad that fancy job of 'ers, she used t' rush round like someone not reight in 'ead. Ah was worried about 'er. Ah'm pleased t' see she's bin gettin' 'em t' muck in wi' cookin' and cleanin'. And she meks sure t' get 'er quiet time in garden, or teks 'erself off fer a ride on that bike of 'ers. And the lake swimmin' must be reight magical wa' wi' no tourists an' all. Aye reight enough, she's teken leaf out o' mah book and we've both found peace 'ere together.

Bushby House garden

Who knows how long this virus will last? During the war, we kept thinking it would be over by the summer, then Christmas, then the next summer. Six years it was in the end. Alice is right. I need to lighten up and not get 'mithered' as she would say, about things I can't control. The big things like Covid, or ash dieback or climate change. And as for the small things like the mention of a new project in the garden, the horses changing their morning routine, or the pigeons getting the courgette plants, well it's just plain silly to worry about those. Go with the flow. I just need to feel good about myself and the way I am living my life. The here and now is what matters.

Asparagus (*Asparagus officinalis*)

Speaking of which, I don't suppose there'll be a beer festival in September this year. The excitement builds as they erect the beer marquee across the road. Then the barrels of real ale arrive one by one, and a local farmer delivers straw bales for folk to sit on. Twinkly lights are put in the trees. It's like a big party that everyone looks forward to. And Alice says she's going to miss the winter film nights at the village hall. She watches as people make their way there, pulling their collars up against the cold. The smell of the one-pot suppers they serve before the film wafts here from over the road. And like in a real cinema, they get ice creams at the interval. Gives her a bit of interest whilst most things are dormant.

I've been noticing recently that I'm not ticking off the weeks and months until my big sleep, like I normally do. I'm realising it's such a waste to wish the days away. Maybe I'm finally learning to live in the moment. Life is to be enjoyed, and that's what I intend to do. Perhaps I need to get over myself and join Alice with her yogic chanting and sun salutations.

CHAPTER 2

Bean (*Phaseolus coccineus*)

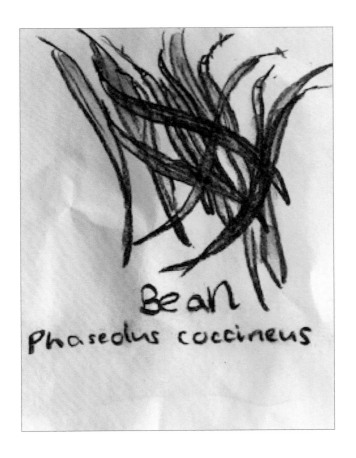

1974 AND 2001

Mr Herring's shop is a particularly large rectangular shed, covered all over with green painted clapboard. It has one window at the front and a car parking space outside. It is the only shop in the lower part of the village where we live. When I ride my green shopper bike the two miles to school, I am only a third of the way up the steep hill as I pass the shop on my right. On the way home, I go faster than the wind. At the top of the hill is a post office and tiny shop run by the parents of one of the girls in my class. Occasionally my mum calls in there for ciggies if she has run out and can't wait until the next trip into town.

She often shares her moral tale with us:

'I thought I was the bee's knees with a fag hanging out of my mouth when I started work and could afford to smoke. Well, everyone did. But it's a disgusting habit and once you start, it's the Devil's own job to stop.'

She finally did and I have heeded the advice. My dad smokes a pipe, circles of smoke rising above his head as he marks his books at night, sitting in the re-covered armchair. He stuffs more tobacco into the end of it, relights it and then makes his lips into a small round shape and sucks hard on the end, like a straw.

There is a counter which runs the length of the shop and it's always covered with boxes of stock. Every square inch is taken. 'I don't know how long some of it has been there,' I overhear my mum saying, when a packet of something is taken home and its contents are rock solid. But we don't complain in our family. We not so quietly suffer and bear it.

Sometimes there is a radio playing modern music when you

go in, but you can't tell where the noise is coming from. Mr Herring switches it off, so he can hear you properly. Dad calls him Bert. He's usually hidden from view initially, though you can hear a disembodied voice saying 'Morning sir' or 'Afternoon sir' in reply to Dad's cheery greeting. He only appears from behind the piles of stuff when you reach the till at the end. He wears a grey cotton coat overall over his shirt and tie. His trousers and shoes stick out the bottom. He has a tiny bit of hair and a large mole over one eyebrow on his wide face. I have never seen a Mrs Herring. Maybe she is buried under the patio, or maybe I am reading too many Roald Dahl books.

The shop smells fusty and slightly damp, like old people, and when the sun shines you can see the dust everywhere. My mum points this out to me. She seems quite focused on dust generally, how a certain light shows it up, how we create it by charging around, how she clears it up every week with a damp cloth and how it comes back before she knows it. 'It's like painting the Forth Bridge', apparently, which seems a confusing metaphor.

There is a rotating stand of vegetable and flower seeds. Whenever I go in with Dad, he pauses by it and twirls it round to remind himself what's there. Generally, he chooses at least two packets from it, which he puts on the counter to pay for along with anything else we need. He is excited at the prospect of new additions to his immaculate vegetable garden. It's Dad's pride and joy, and he spends hours in it, whistling away as he listens to the ball-by-ball test match commentary on the radio. And now, to top it all, Mr Herring has recently started stocking garden twine.

'Now that's just what I need. Do you know, my runner beans have gone mad this year. I've never seen them grow quite so enormous. This will be just the job for tying them back on the canes.'

When we get home, he hastens outside and starts cutting lengths of the twine with his secateurs. 'Here, hold these for me, will you?' I go to stand next to him and hand the lengths of twine to him one by one as he reattaches the rampant plants. After he has finished, he puts what's left on the roll back in his well-ordered garden shed.

The shop's freezer is stocked with ice lollipops and ice cream in the summer. In the warmer months, I linger next to it, doing my wide-eyed 'I've been a good girl and surely I deserve one of these' hopeful but not expectant look. I must never expect because that means I will become spoilt. On the top shelf are random things Mr Herring has spotted in the local cash and carry in Mablethorpe that he thinks might get snapped up. One day I see two girls' vanity cases, one blue and one red, that weren't there the last time I went in. I hope Dad will take ages talking to Mr Herring because I just want to stand and stare at them, thinking what I would do if I owned one, where I would take it, how I would carry it.

It's not my birthday or Christmas any time soon, and even the small case would be way beyond my pocket money stash. Although I would never ask how much they are because it feels presumptuous. Nevertheless, every time I go into the shop, I check whether they are still there on the top shelf and am at least relieved that no one else has bought them because a miracle could happen, like a fairy godmother coming along.

I daydream about what there might be inside the cases, maybe a mirror or a little brush or some secret pockets for the few but very precious things I have. Mum says I do a lot of daydreaming.

On Friday after school, I go to band practice. I sit on the front row because I am a clarinettist. I love it, though it can be a bit stressful when we have the melody and forget to come in on time or mess it up. But Mr Willetts is quite patient unless we are coming up to a concert and then he gets a bit fiercer if we make mistakes. My first love Robert also sits on the front row and plays the cornet. We glance over to each other during practice. Once rehearsal is over, I pack away my local authority clarinet and head to my dad's office at the front of the school where he is still working. I will get my own clarinet on my 18th birthday.

Dad's study has 'Headmaster' on the door just in case anyone is in any doubt. It is always tidy, and he sits behind a huge desk with a leather top and an ink pen and bottle in the middle. He intends it to be an imposing space he tells me, when I ask why it is so big for so few papers on it. At the end of morning assembly, he always concludes by saying, 'After assembly I would like to see the following people in my office,' and then recites the list of shame. He sweeps out of the hall in his university gown, whilst everyone stands up.

Once the entire U15 hockey team is on the list of shame and we trundle up the covered way to stand outside his office. This is my first experience of being the other side of that desk. I look at the floor throughout, unable to meet his eye. We have all been reported by the PE staff for very bad sportsmanship on an away fixture and we have let the school down, ourselves down, our parents down, and I'm not sure who else, but the list is long.

When I go into his office after school to get a lift home, he is signing letters or on the phone. He either signals me to come in or to wait outside, but he always winks at me come what may when I peep around the door. I will come to reflect that having your dad as the headmaster of your school is not an easy gig. For now, I never really think about it. I've never known any different.

During the school day, he treats me like anyone else in the school. I am expected to call him 'Sir' in class or in the corridors. If I occasionally bump into him when he is doing one of his impromptu tours of the school and I am by myself, he always gives me a conspiratorial smile, which makes me feel very special, but then he puts his headmaster look straight back on in case someone else appears. I come to realise there are some pupils who don't feel the same way about him as I do. The worst will be when I am in the sixth form and three lads, who all 'have history' with my dad, decide to tie me up and leave me on the floor in the common room as revenge for their previous treatment. My best friend will come to my rescue, but I will never forget the humiliation. Probably they have been on the receiving end of the cane I know is in his office.

He takes no prisoners when it comes to upholding standards and dealing with misdemeanours. The cane is next to his bookcases in the corner of his study. It looks like something you'd find in his vegetable patch at home. I wonder how it feels to be hit with it. Boys only, never girls. Reserved for the worst misdemeanours or serial offenders. On the buttocks. They bend over his desk. He shows it to me because I ask to see it one day. I am puzzled how such a kind man could have an instrument of torture in his office, but I know it is as safe in his hands as in anyone's.

At home, my dad hates bad feeling and conflict, and I will only ever have a few arguments with him. One will be when I am considering whether to follow in his footsteps and train as a teacher. His claim that the teaching profession has somehow become diluted by 'too many part-time women in it who are not principal bread winners' will seem outrageous to me. The idea that any profession should be first and foremost the domain of men will make me feel like we belong to different worlds, never mind generations.

After he has finished what he is doing in his study, and I never complain no matter how long I have to wait, we cross the road to where the car is parked. I sit in the front because it is just me and Dad. I love it when it is the two of us, because he talks to me as if I am very grown up. We always stop at Mr Herring's shop on the way home on a Friday. When I start to learn to drive in a few years' time, my L-plates proudly displayed on the rear bumper, Dad will be sitting in the passenger seat looking calmly ahead, as I grip the steering wheel and proceed to commit all manner of road user errors. The most memorable will be one Friday evening when I misjudge my entry into the driveway of our house and crash the car at speed into the gatepost. Normally if I do something stupid, Dad quietly says, 'And what do you do for an encore?'

in his rather dry humorous way. But even he will be totally speechless as he picks up bits of car from the gravel drive.

Friday night is whoopee night, my parents always say. They go to the pub after tea and we are left at home either with a babysitter or, when we are old enough, by ourselves. For us kids, to make it special, we are allowed three choices of boiled sweets from the dozens of jars in Mr Herring's shop. The sweets are weighed out and put in paper bags. It is difficult to choose because they must last all weekend and there will be no more until the following Friday.

Dad is not only the local headmaster but also chair of the parish council. So, he gets his ear bent about all things to do with education, but also all-important local village matters, like drains, road surfaces, streetlights, and signs. Dad always engages respectfully and earnestly with Mr Herring and anyone else who happens to be in the shop for that matter.

I use the waiting time profitably by sizing up the tall plastic jars and their contents, scanning over them in case there is anything new Mr Herring might have picked up from his weekly cash and carry shop that hadn't been there the previous week.

My favourites are rhubarb and custard. I love the tang of the rhubarb and the sweetness of the custard. It is like eating a delicious pudding. They are extremely hard, meaning they last for ever and leave a pink and yellow residue on your tongue. And my brother and sister don't like them much, which means I get more for myself. They prefer strawberry bon bons and sherbet lemons, so we get those too.

When we get home, the three bags are put ceremoniously

on the 1960's mantlepiece in the lounge. Providing it's after teatime, no limits are put on how many times we can help ourselves. On Friday nights, pretty much anything goes as my parents are always in a good mood. After a while, the sweets stick to the sides of the bags and then you get a mouthful of paper every time you have one. Soon it's *It's a Knockout* or *The Goodies* on the BBC. I need to watch it because everyone will be talking about it on the 'Boneshaker' bus on Monday morning.

We have a couple of regular babysitters. Mum's friend Daphne told her about Gladys Wilson, and she is 'a godsend'. She also cleans occasionally for Mum, 'when the house gets into an indescribable mess and you can see the dust everywhere'. She lives in a tiny upstairs bedsit in Spilsby, two miles away. We run up the narrow stairs next to the hardware shop to go and tell her Mum or Dad is waiting outside in the car for her. She lives by herself and her flat is always absolutely freezing cold. You can see your breath as you go in, and she has blankets everywhere to cover herself with.

She is very thin, with false teeth that clatter around her mouth and small metal rimmed glasses. She seems sad, I have never seen her smile, but she is kind and gentle and lets us stay up beyond our allotted bedtimes. The slightly sickly-sweet smell of her perfume is overwhelming and reminds me of Alice, my Grandma Farmer. They refer to her as Gladys when they talk about her, but my parents always call her Miss Wilson to her face. She wears a cardigan and skirt, and she sits in the upright chair in our lounge, as if she hasn't earnt the right to flop into one of the comfier armchairs which have recently been re-covered in a green and orange flowery material.

We have another babysitter sometimes, Mrs East, a farmer's wife who is much jollier. She always sits in one of the comfy, recently re-covered armchairs and knocks the removable protective arm caps off with her bulky frame. She lowers herself down with a great big sigh and, as her creaking body hits the springs, we get a sight of her white bloomers underneath her skirt which extend nearly down to her knees. My brother keeps dropping things on the floor so she will have to get up and then sit down again and we get a further sighting. We can get away with quite a lot when we have babysitters as they won't complain to our parents unless we are really bad. So, we make up stories about what we are allowed to do and the programmes our parents say we can watch. But sometimes things get out of hand and, as the oldest, I feel I need to keep my giddy siblings in check. I'll almost certainly be the one to get into trouble if words are had at the end of the evening, because 'I'm old enough to know better'. However, my brother and sister don't take kindly to being restrained by someone they regard as without authority and add my interventions to their list of grievances to be aired at some appropriate future date.

Sometimes we wake up when my parents come back from the pub, such are the hijinks and loud voices, particularly if they come back with friends. My sister often gets up, entertains the assembled crowd, and then has to be persuaded back to bed. I prefer to keep myself to myself and find the raised voices, raucous laughter and high spirits rather alarming. Anyway, I know that if I go into the lounge, I will be asked loads of questions, any normal filters removed under the influence of several pints of beer.

In years to come, despite all good intention and resolve, sweets will remain an important currency when it comes to dealing with my own children. When a child screams in the chair of a crowded barber's shop on a Saturday morning, I am prepared, with a packet of Opal Fruits stashed in my pocket. When there are fisticuffs in the back of the car on a long journey, and we are bored of playing the number plates game, I produce a tin of mixed fruit travel sweets bought at the last motorway service station. Or when the complaining on a walk or cycle ride becomes too intolerable, I stop and look in my rucksack for the Werther's Originals I know will shut them up.

Friday is also sweetie day for my boys. I never travel with work on Fridays and use it as a catch-up day for outstanding emails, calls and reports, as well as trying to get things organised for the weekend. In fact, even though it is my day off, it is equally if not busier than the other days. I try to be the perfect housewife, mum and professional, all at the same time. By the time I have gone round the supermarket, come home and put all the groceries away, and then caught up on the phone with difficult clients, interspersed with some household sorting out, I am shattered. I always have good intentions of making flapjacks or cupcakes like other mums do, but it never happens. Instead, I choose some crowd-pleasing cakes from the local bakers, generally opting for ones with smarties on them or chocolate piping.

Sometimes I try to have a power nap just for a few moments before setting off around 3pm to walk the short distance to school. This is the most anticipated moment of the week for me. I catch up with people I know whilst waiting in the playground, but at the same time watch out for the three little heads emerging at different times down the steps, skipping and smiling or glum and foot stamping dependent on what kind of day they have had. Matt's face lights up when he remembers it's Friday and I'm there, and he comes to nuzzle his head against my arm, whilst his younger brothers dance around me trying to talk at once. Josh smiles coquettishly as he appears from the classroom and runs towards me with his arms out and I hear Tim's 'Mummeeeeeee' before I see him. I gather up my precious flock, their school bags, PE kits and any pictures, paintings or models and we turn towards the school gates.

As we walk, they shout up at me whatever is the most important thing. 'I got a new reading book' or 'We had chips for lunch' or often 'It's sweetie day'. It is generally not good news if the teacher asks to see you, and today I've escaped the walk of shame up the steps and into a classroom to be quietly reminded I do not have perfect children. I see other mums looking at me, and someone ventures up, 'So nice to see you. Wasn't the concert lovely on Wednesday? Oh no, sorry, I forgot you weren't there, you must have been at work. Your nanny was there, wasn't she? Oh, what a shame, you missed it. Your boys were just so good in it. It was the best yet.' The guilt knife is further twisted inside me.

We head to the park, but first we have to go through the after-school Friday ritual of the sweet shop. The boys have an allotted sum of money that they can spend. This amount is subject to downward adjustment if there has been bad behaviour at home, but I usually forget by how much. They don't, especially if others should be getting less than them. The shop is small, with shelves on each side and central piles of stock to boot. At any one time at that hour on Friday there are at least a dozen children all on the same mission and several waiting outside as well.

Each takes a paper bag and walks solemnly the length of the bottom shelves where the open boxes of brightly coloured curly jelly worms, love heart tubes, fruit salad bars, gobstoppers, sugared mice and liquorish sticks are. Sometimes they need to do more than one round to check they have not missed anything. The younger children have one eye on their own bag and another on the bags of the older children as they are wilier about getting the most sweets for their money.

I point to the jars of old-fashioned boiled sweets on the shelves above. They remind me of Fridays when I was young and we used to go to the village shop after band practice. 'What about those?' I say, 'Look, they've got rhubarb and custards. Those were my favourites when I was a girl,' but they don't even raise their heads to look.

The shopkeeper is very patient as heads pop up and a chorus of voices asks all at the same time about different items, 'and how much is this one?' The older ones are better at maths and can keep a running total of their bag contents, but the smaller children just gather away, led by delight not budget. Usually at least one bag bursts and the entire contents drop on the floor. Then someone treads on them.

The most tired amongst them ends up in tears or howls in protest that it's not fair. From the side lines I watch the drama unfold like a weary producer of some predictable weekly soap opera.

We walk to the park, the children's heads in their sweetie bags, with largely unheeded reminders to wait for the lollipop lady or the green man before crossing the roads. Once in the park, any last attempt at keeping control is futile as they run for freedom in three different directions, discarding their unwanted coats, scarves and gloves behind them on the soggy ground. I go round retrieving the scattered items of clothing. They throw themselves on swings, slides and roundabouts regardless of whether they are already occupied or moving. I rest for a moment on one of the slatted park benches. No one looks in imminent danger of falling off anything. My eyelids are so heavy, I let them briefly close out of pity for them.

Eventually it is time to go back for tea. I try to persuade them all to get their outer layers back on again. With luck, when I get home there are no urgent messages from the office that cannot wait until Monday. Only teatime, bath time and story time to get through now. I hope the green Saab carrying their dad might sweep into the drive a bit earlier tonight as it's Friday, though the pre-weekend traffic coming out of Manchester is usually bad, so my hopes aren't high. How long until bedtime? I whip up some pasta and sauce for tea, and then today it's jam tarts from Hill's Bakery in the village for afters. Tim once ate so many of them he was sick in the bath afterwards, so I keep careful count as they are consumed.

Bean (*Phaseolus coccineus*)

I clear up whilst they watch a bit of telly. I am now but a shadow of my high functioning self and my only thought is of a glass of chilled white wine as it is approaching 6.30pm. 'Come on you lot, upstairs for bath time,' I say more than once, my head twisted round the sitting room door. And as they finally troop out backwards, their faces still pointing towards the TV, I hear the front door opening and an energetic, 'Hello everyone. I'm home. Did you have a good day darling? I've just got a call to make and then I'll be right with you.' Heard that one before. Better take my wine with me.

CHAPTER 3

Brussels Sprout
(*Brassica oleracea var. gemmifera*)

1975

Girls' school cloakrooms

It's bedlam in here when the girls come and leave their belongings in the morning. Screeching, gossiping, and giggling. Then the assembly bell goes and silence falls. We are situated in the old part of the school between the history and geography rooms. There are four lines of hooks with benches underneath. A jumble of coats, hockey sticks, domestic science baskets and kitbags. How they ever manage to find anything beats me. Then down a few stairs are the loos, washbasins and mirrors where the girls endlessly comb their hair, put on forbidden mascara and check their teenage skins for unwelcome pimples.

These two are best friends. Today they arrive at the same time after afternoon lessons to collect their things. They never draw breath. One of them complains about the geography teacher.

'I don't believe it. He's gone and done it again. Always waits until after the final bell goes before setting homework. He's given us loads.'

The other is searching frantically in her games kitbag. 'Can't find my other hockey sock. Must have left it in the changing rooms after games. Can we have a look on the way? I've got a match on Saturday. I'll never hear the end of it if I've lost it.'

The Deputy Head, a large cat-loving lady who waddles around in polyester dresses that cling to her, is on the war path.

'Come on girls, get a move on. Less dawdling now. The bell went ten minutes ago.'

They get their coats on before heading out of the playground and down the lane at the back to where the buses wait.

Brussels Sprout (*Brassica oleracea var. gemmifera*)

We swagger out of the cloakroom and down to the secondary modern school in our grammar school uniforms to the line of buses. We come home on one called 'The Boneshaker'. The bus passes endless fields of cabbages, leeks, Brussels sprouts and potatoes as it drops children like food parcels next to clusters of houses on the road that leads down the Fens. The vegetables are sold fresh at the local market every Tuesday. Huge quantities of them, freshly dug up and stacked in great mounds.

Mum goes there and loads her wicker basket up with a week's worth of accompaniments to the meals she has carefully planned. We have been fed a diet of leafy green stuff ever since we can remember. 'Brussels sprouts? Your favourite vegetable was really Brussels sprouts?' my incredulous children will say in about 25 years as I tell them I had no choice but to eat them and eventually came to like them. It was that or nothing. The moral of the story will be lost on them.

The Boneshaker stops right outside our house for me, my brother and sister to get off. My best friend Dawn's house is the next stop after ours. A standard issue school bus, its blue shell is perched on top of the wheelbase and has two sets of wooden benches lengthways, girls on one side, boys on the other. Normally last in the bus line, it is like the relative you feel embarrassed by.

The girls from Sibsey and Stickney go home on a cool green double decker bus, contracted out from a firm in Boston. Leather seats and a bell you ring when you want to get off. They wave down to us mere mortals from the back row of the top deck. Their bus is usually last to arrive in the mornings, so they saunter into assembly late, soaking up attention from the already seated rest of the school. Life would almost certainly be several notches better if I lived on that bus route. I once mentioned it in passing at teatime and was given short shrift, 'Oh for goodness sake. What does it matter what bus you come home on? Whatever next?'

Dawn and I sit side by side on the bus home. Despite being joined at the hip, as our mums say, we never run out of things to say or giggle about. My mum can't bear the giggling and wishes we would stop it. She imitates it in an exaggerated high-pitched voice. We discuss the disco next Saturday night, and which of our houses we are going to get ready in. Dawn says her mum is doing a nightshift at the old people's home where she is the manager.

'I'll ask my mum if you can come for tea and stay over,' I suggest. 'What are you wearing?'

'Don't know, probably my new jeans and tie waisted shirt.'

I've put a couple of darts in the waistband of my only pair of jeans and now the stiff triangles of fabric cut into me. It's either these or a pair of beige Marks and Spencer crimplene trousers, which make my bum look big. My cheesecloth shirt, with a tie waist is a bit on the short side but it will have to do. My mum won't say no to Dawn staying over, and my dad will say 'Right let's be having you' as he grabs his car keys to drive us to the disco. Dawn's dad died last year. He was kind and funny, but I didn't go to the funeral because it 'wasn't appropriate'. Mum said the crematorium was full of people and Dawn was very brave. No one ever talks about him or the fact he is dead.

The girls from Sibsey and Stickney have weekend jobs in Boston and get their clothes on the Saturday market. Rails and rails of them apparently. Dead cheap. As we walk to the bus stop, I look longingly at their full ankle length skirts and flat moccasin shoes with crepe soles. They wear the fashionable short waisted jumpers made from synthetic material, but Mum says wool wears better and the others look cheap and nasty. My pocket money will not extend to buying new clothes. Dawn and I talk about getting waitressing jobs next summer in a fish and chip shop in Skegness. 'It will teach you the value of money' I am reassured.

The Boneshaker is a jungle where a predator could pounce at any moment. Half the time we don't know what the older girls are talking or sniggering about, but we don't let on. Tonight, they taunt us with, 'Bet you don't know what this is,' as they make their index finger and thumb on one hand into a circle and then poke a finger from the other hand through the hole. We giggle. Occasionally the driver glances up at his rear mirror and shouts, 'Hey up, keep it down you lot.'

We trudge up the drive after being dropped off. The key is under the brick and we let ourselves in. The cat is waiting, thank goodness. My mum is always fraught with anxiety about the cat, ever since the last one got run over. We drop our bags inside the front door. It's freezing cold. It is a dormer bungalow, but my mum always uses its generic name when the boiler goes out, 'This house is like a bloody fridge.' Please let the boiler still have signs of life. I see the tiniest pink colour inside. I poke it with the long thin implement like my parents do, and then put some rolled up newspaper in to get the flames going, followed by some more solid fuel.

Then I go into the pantry. I look in the chest freezer for things that I can eat frozen, because I am starving, and teatime is a long way off. In one of the top baskets are different flavours of Victoria sandwich sponges, made by Mum on one of her days off. Orange, lemon, chocolate, coffee and walnut, and plain. Sliced into portions ready to be taken and eaten. I take two portions of orange cake. It's already got pieces missing, so there's less chance of being found out.

On the windowsill in the pantry are rows of demijohns and plastic tubes, stained red. The entire family is required to go blackberry picking at certain times of the year and not allowed back in the car until we have each filled a whole bucketful, which apparently goes nowhere when you are making wine. Mum and Dad make gallons of the stuff. It looks and tastes disgusting, but they are more mellow after it.

I imagine how life would be with a fringe. I loop my heavy hair around my hairbrush and lift it to fringe height on my forehead so I can imagine what it would be like. 'Don't be so vain,' Mum says when she catches me looking in the mirror. She reminds me of 'that ghastly afro perm', which far from giving my lank hair a bit more body, was the first properly traumatic thing ever to happen to me. I came home from the hairdressers with my hood up in case anyone saw me, burst into tears, and went to my bedroom. 'Well, if you try to change what nature gave you, what do you expect?' Dad says unhelpfully.

Eventually I am told to come out of my room for tea. 'It's only hair for goodness sake. Pull yourself together.' When I eventually go into the dining room, my dad puts his hand over his mouth and smirks like he does when he is pulling my leg. 'Oh, come on. Where is your sense of humour?' he laughs, and the rest of the pack join in. No one has known misery quite like this.

'She is neither fish nor fowl,' I hear Mum say on the telephone to one of her friends, which apparently means I'm neither fully adult nor still a child. I'm also repeatedly told that 'I am so clumsy'. I sometimes do feel that my hands and feet aren't properly connected to me, like they have minds of their own. And I am so much taller than most of my friends, towering above them like some gawky giant, just when I want to blend into the background and not be too visible. I don't mean to be argumentative, but I am of an age when I don't always agree with what's being said. Sometimes I can't keep my opinions to myself and I've learnt that they are not always welcome. I am accused of 'always having to have the last word' and want to argue with the logic of this statement, as it's not me saying it.

My long hair gets lank and greasy. My mum says it looks so awful when girls have hair all over their faces, so I tie it back in a ponytail. I buy *Jackie* magazine every week with my pocket money. It's essential reading and gives many helpful hints on various topics, like how to make your hair look less greasy by putting some talcum powder near the parting. The letters to the agony aunt are usually about periods or boyfriends or sex. All of it seems a bit irrelevant to me right now. It's usually got some tips on hiding love bites. *Jackie* magazine recommends either wearing a polo neck jumper or using some makeup, neither of which would conform with the school uniform policy. Some girls wear them like trophies, clearly visible above the collars of their white shirts. My mum thinks they are common, 'For goodness sake, what do those girls think they look like with those dreadful massive bruises all over their necks?'

Before the French exchange last year, all the girls in my form brought home a letter from the Deputy Headmistress about periods, in case 'it happens' whilst we are in France. Our mums were instructed to equip us with belts and sanitary towels to put in our suitcases. This growing up lark suddenly feels less than attractive. Mum tells me she thinks 'it won't be long now'. It will be like gaining entrance to some elite club. Most of the Stickney and Sibsey girls have started their periods and miss the freezing cold showers after hockey when they are 'on'.

I go into my bedroom to see if my spots have got any bigger since I last looked at them in the school cloakrooms. It is hard to get up close to the mirror attached to the dressing table to get a proper look, but I cannot resist squeezing a couple of the bigger ones, hoping they will be less visible by tomorrow. I rummage through my wardrobe to see if anything new has magically appeared in there for the disco next weekend.

Time to start my homework. I go down the hall towards the dining room, past where the phone sits on a recessed shelf at the curved end of the built-in double cupboards that house everyone's coats. And the 20 or so portable typewriters that Mum loads up into the boot of the car every Tuesday when she drives to Skegness to teach typing at the adult education centre. There is only one phone in the house.

When making an outgoing call, after you have placed your finger in the hole of the first number, it rotates noisily, alerting everyone in the household. When the phone occasionally rings for me, I go and stand by the phone to speak to whoever it is.

Rarely do I get any privacy. It seems that the whole house joins in my conversation. Either Mum or Dad start moving between the hall, the kitchen and the sitting room, or my brother and sister deliberately wander down the hall from their bedrooms so they can earwig what's going on.

Before getting my books out, I have been careful to put the felt cloth on the prized dining room table for fear of scratching it. I set everything out, decide on the order I'm going to do the work I have been set, and then get a drink before starting. As I go past the phone, it starts to ring. I tut as I stomp outside to get it. 'Hello, Spilsby 2439,' I say as I put the receiver close to my ear.

It's my mum and she is just about to leave the solicitor's office where she is secretary to the senior partner.

'I'm putting the cover on my typewriter now. I'll be home in about half an hour. Is everything alright? Was the cat waiting outside when you got home?' I reassure her that everything is fine, and the cat was waiting outside.

'Is the boiler still going?'

'Yes, I used the poker on it, then put some more fuel in it.'

'Good. That's good news. Ok see you all shortly. It's the toasty kind of tea tonight, something nice and easy. Bye for now.'

Most nights we have a proper dinner with everything cooked from scratch. Steak and kidney pie or liver hotpot are my two favourites. With piles of creamy mashed potato and gravy poured over the top, and if it's my lucky day, Brussels sprouts as well. On a day when Mum is working, she has usually prepared something in advance, or we have toasty tea. We get two slices of toast each and then choose between toppings, either poached eggs, bacon, or cheese. On the days we have toasty tea, we normally have cake for pudding.

On the way home from work, Mum stops the car outside Dad's study at the front of the school where he is the headmaster and beeps the horn three times to let him know she is there. He switches the light off in his study, picks up his big bunch of keys, and his briefcase containing the books he needs to mark this evening, and then comes out the front entrance of the school. He turns round, locks up and after he has double checked the door, he gets into the passenger seat. Then they drive home, through the gate posts I will crash into in a few years' time when I start learning to drive, and screech to a halt on the gravel drive. I hear the two front car doors bang shut, footsteps up the path and then the front door bursts open.

My dad puts his briefcase down in the hall and my mum heads like a launched missile into the kitchen with her basket of shopping. She barely draws breath. She announces to no one in particular, 'Christ what a day. I need a sherry!' Dad puts the radio on. After about half an hour, I hear the gateleg table being scraped along the floor out of the pantry into the kitchen, where we eat on weekday nights. The clattering of pots and pans reaches a crescendo and eventually Mum or Dad calls 'Right, come on now, all of you stop what you are doing and get your tea.'

Dad always sits at the far end of the table. He wears his V-neck sweater over his shirt and tie. We all eat our tea very quickly. 'Are you trying to take the pattern off the plate?' my mum says. After tea, the conversation turns to our much-anticipated holiday in France, like it always does about this time of the year, because it's getting ever closer. Dad's love affair with France started when he took the train and ferry and first went over to the Sarthe area in the north west of the country to set up the exchange with our school. He had never been abroad before. He was wined and dined by the head teacher and has never looked back since. And then we went to France as a family for the first time. And have been every summer since. Anything French that can be eaten or drunk is revered. The whole packing system for the car is designed around being able to fit the maximum legal wine allowance into it when we go to the hypermarket at Calais before the ferry home.

Dad likes to update us on the exact timescale. He leans back and grins, 'Well now, it's only ten weeks, three days and six hours until we get on the ferry.' Yesterday, the same ritual, only the tally was one day more. He gleefully slaps his hand down on the table for extra emphasis and reminds us in case we have forgotten since yesterday, 'And this year we are going for three whole weeks.' He is the cat that has got the cream off the top of the milk. Every night the discussion is about another item on his extensive pre-holiday 'to do' list. Yesterday, it was the sorry state of the French franc against the pound and whether he should wait to buy some currency or get it now before the situation gets worse. The day before, the items he needs to get at the cash and carry to take with us on the camping trip. I lose interest as soon as dried asparagus soup is mentioned.

Tonight's topic does not seem worthy of lengthy discussion either.

'I need to sort out the 5-star car insurance so I can get my green card.' As if we need any justification for this, he lists the possible disasters.

'We could have a breakdown, or worse still an accident. Someone could reverse into us outside one of those huge hypermarkets, or the car could get broken into. Or we could have a mechanical issue and they might not be able to get the spare part straight away.'

Whilst I have been drifting off, the conversation has taken a worrying turn.

'You kids don't know how lucky you are. We never went abroad when we were your age, never even dreamt of it. Money doesn't grow on trees you know. We would just like some helpful children between now and then, without having to ask you so many times.' I nod and start to get up and clear the table.

But Dad's not quite finished organising yet. He revisits the familiar topic of when we need to leave home to catch the ferry. Dad hates being late, so he builds in extra time to mitigate against anything that could go wrong.

'I think we need to leave by 5.00am at the latest.' Mum is ready for him,

'5.00am, that's absurd. Why do we need to leave at that ridiculous time in the morning? We're always hanging around for hours because we get to places too early. And there are no facilities there to speak of.'

The discussion is unresolved, to be recommenced the next evening. I scrape back my stool and stand up to collect the dirty plates. Mum gets up, sweeps out of the kitchen with the remnants of her glass of homemade blackberry wine in hand and says, 'I don't know whose turn it is to wash up, but I'm not doing it. I'm going to put my feet up and I don't want to hear any fuss and bother about who is going to do what. Do you hear me?'

We begrudgingly clear the table. My dad hovers long enough to check there is a plan about who is going to wash, who will dry and who will put away.

'Come on you three, that's enough, you heard what your mum said about helping. Now no nonsense, just get on with it without a fuss.'

He starts marking books in the lounge next door. We bicker about who did what yesterday, and what is or isn't fair. 'Bagsy wash,' says my sister, because then she will finish first. But she never changes the washing up water halfway through, so bits of egg, sardine and soggy bread cling to the cutlery and the plates when she puts them on the draining rack. My brother bagsies drying but fails to rinse off the soapy suds or food bits properly. That leaves me to redo their jobs before 'putting away'. The tragedy of being the eldest.

When the argy bargy becomes noisy, my dad reappears with his headmaster's voice, 'This is very disappointing. You're all going to be taken to France for three weeks this year. The least you can do is help without so much fuss and splutter. Your mum works very hard and it's not much to ask. Now come on. Play the game.'

We are shamed into silently completing our tasks, not missing the opportunity to give each other a little poke with a fork or a jostle as an elbow comes up to dry a plate. 'Ow. That hurt.' Followed by, 'Shut up, they'll hear us, and we'll get into more trouble.'

When we finish the washing up, I complete my homework for the night. Afterwards, I go through into the lounge where the TV stands in the corner. We have our weekly viewing routine. *Coronation Street* on Mondays and Wednesdays and *Crossroads* every day except Mondays. *It's a Knockout* on Fridays when Mum and Dad are out. Dad likes cowboy films and Diana Rigg. Mum likes anything with singing in it. On Sundays, we watch *Songs of Praise* in the evening. Mum sings along loudly to the hymns, which she knows from years of going to church. As she hits her top soprano notes with gusto, we stifle our giggles. She gets mad because we are being so childish and ruining her enjoyment. Dad watches the news most nights after we've gone to bed.

My mum always sits in the same flowery chair by the fireplace, her unravelling ball of wool and half-finished glass of blackberry wine by her side. As she knits, she peers over the top of her glasses at the television. My new navy school jumper is growing from her needles every night with its fashionable deep welt, and I am desperate for it to be finished. 'Can you just put the noise up a bit,' she says to whoever is sitting nearest the TV. She stops the clacking of the needles momentarily so she can reassure herself that it is loud enough, then nods and resumes.

Dad sits in the other flowery chair, his red pen hovering over the diminishing pile of exercise books. The stack of finished marking is in a neat pile next to him. Occasionally he sighs as he corrects multiple errors in one book, then looks at the front cover to see who the offender is. We usually lie on the floor, making the place look untidy. 'Put those cushions back where they belong, when you're finished with them,' we are told.

I must learn my French verbs for a test tomorrow. I have

half memorised them and test myself between *Crossroads* and *Coronation Street*. Before the news comes on, I go to my room and get ready for bed. I pull my brown nylon quilted bedspread, dyed to match the feature wall, up to my nose which is already cold to the touch. I lay my school uniform out at the foot of the other twin bed, so I can reach it from under the covers if I shuffle forwards. I draw the mustard curtains of the bay window because I don't like to think someone is peering in from the dark outside when I have the centre light on.

I can just about hear the theme tune heralding the start of the BBC News when I eventually switch the light out. I recite my French verbs one more time under my breath to reassure myself I haven't forgotten them and then I do a quick mental check to see if there is anything else that I need to be worrying about. The last thing I do before I go to sleep is to put my fingertips where I squeezed my spots earlier. I check how much the bumps have gone down and hope that by the time I get on 'The Boneshaker' in the morning, they will have all but disappeared.

CHAPTER 4

Cabbage (*Brassica oleracea*)

Cabbage

Brassica oleracea var.
capitata

VARIOUS DATES 1962–1969

Some people it seems are born and, from the word go, instinctively claim their voice and place in the world. Like it is their entitlement and their right. It wasn't like that for me. In the beginning, I am likened to a cabbage. Indeed, this vegetable with few redeeming features is my nickname. As soon as I am old enough to think about these things, I look at the one in the vegetable rack and imagine it being me.

Personally, I can't see any similarity. But I'm told it is an affectionate name that came about as a result of my difficult entry into the world. After my mother had laboured for 24 hours, I came out feet first with the aid of forceps, and my head was unsurprisingly misshapen and lop-sided. The final characteristic that likened me to a member of the brassica family was my wrinkly, uneven skin. Everyone always laughs when Dad tells the story of why I am called 'Cabbage'. Joint recipients of everyone's mirth, this is probably how my affinity with inanimate objects begins.

Born in a snowy January, I spend most of my early weeks in a shiny new Silver Cross pram. I am rarely content. My dad has learnt to rock me in it whilst reading a book in the middle of another sleepless night. I lie in it in the garden, where I glower at passers-by if they so much as peer in to get a look at me. From about six in the evening, I cry loudly and inconsolably in it, for no apparent reason. My face is crumpled and red, my back arched, and my legs doubled up.

No sooner do I get rid of colic than my sister is conceived. She arrives when I am 18 months old. Dad gets a new job and Mum thinks we need to move to a bigger house. My sister, the new occupant of the pram, comes into the world having absorbed the 'how to be a perfect baby book' cover to cover. She is quieter and sunnier than I was. I continue to glower at everyone as I sit on my rug on the lawn, whilst she lies there like the queen, as to the manor born, holding court to any passers-by.

We move to Humberston Avenue into a house with small square-paned windows. There is a driveway down the side and a long thin garden to the rear. One of the bedrooms has a sloping orange wall. I share a room with my sister. We have pink flowery bedspreads.

I spend most of my time in the garden or riding my bike up and down the drive. Getting my stabilisers off is a proud moment, and Dad warns me I may be a bit wobbly to begin with, until I find my balance.

Maroon Austin Cambridge car

I'm his pride and joy. He polishes me every Saturday and then leans back to check he hasn't missed a bit. I am a good-looking car, and he is a handsome fella, so we are a good match. But honestly, can't he see there's a disaster waiting to happen. He's been encouraging the little girl to take the stabilisers off her bike, 'You won't fall off. I'll give you a push and then you need to pedal hard and build up some speed. It'll help you balance better.' I hear him asking her if she is ready. The driveway is narrow, and I am a substantial car, so there's not much margin for error as she goes past me. There's a worried look on her face. She knows how much her dad loves me. He crouches down behind her in front of the garage at the end of the drive. 'Ready, steady, go,' he shouts and launches her and the bike forward. Just at the very moment she gets level with me, she starts to wobble, but she's going fast so she can't stop. Ouch, that hurt. Her handlebars have scratched me. Right the way along the rear passenger door. What a mess. He puts his head in his hands. And she wishes Father Christmas had never left her beloved bike under the tree.

My sister continues to be a problem and has taken to playing with my toys. This 'learning to share' thing seems very one way. Every time I start to play nicely with something, lost in my own little world of imagining inanimate objects talking to me, she has to spoil things. My Tiny Tears doll is the most precious thing I have, and when she gets taken from me, it is the final straw. There is a spare pillowcase in our wardrobe. I take it out and put all my treasured possessions inside. From now on, I always keep the sack of toys with me.

The sack gets bigger and bigger and bumps along behind me on the stairs as I go down. I go upstairs facing the wrong way, so I can drag it up with me, using both hands. Mum says, 'Really this is getting ridiculous, that sack is soon going to be bigger than you are.'

Bonfire Night is one of my favourite nights of the year. The garden is lit up by the lights from the house and the glow of the bonfire beyond the hedge. Mum is in the kitchen. She leans over a pot on the cooker and then turns round to chat to people who are gathered in there. 'Norman loves nothing more than a good fire. Hopefully, we won't have to bother the fire service this evening, because he does have form.' (Laughter.) Rising to her audience, 'Oh yes, he once set the entire house on fire when he left the chip pan unattended on the stove.'

Cabbage (*Brassica oleracea*)

I look longingly at the paper bag filled with bonfire toffee. 'The fireworks will start soon. Put your boots and hat on and go and find Dad.' Mum sees me looking at the sweets. 'Go on then, help yourself.' Mouth stuffed full of a big piece of it, I ask for some help getting my boots on. 'They do seem a bit tight, I don't believe it, your feet must have grown again. Every time I look at her, she has grown,' she laughs to the assembled company. Through the window, I see the bonfire flames are now shooting up into the sky. I watch the glowing embers fall back down. Some land on the hedge and I wonder if we too will need the fire engine, like in my mum's story.

As I head out into the garden, I hear Mum say, 'She is going to have an operation soon. I hope it will all be alright. She gets terrible catarrh, poor thing, and blocked ears. Doctor Burke thinks it's best to have her adenoids taken out before she starts school in January.' She doesn't sound her normal matter of fact self, so I feel a bit worried, but decide not to let it spoil everything.

I make my way to the bottom of the first bit of garden. Beyond the hedge, in what is normally the vegetable patch, I can see Dad's smiling face of concentration in the reflection of the bonfire. He prods the fire at the bottom every now and again with his fork. I am waiting patiently. 'When will the fireworks start?' I ask. 'Soon. We'll just wait for everyone to come outside.' He takes the fireworks out of the box and starts reading the instructions using the light of his torch.

At last, I am told to stand well back and I see Dad bending down behind the hedge. I hear a whooshing noise, and then suddenly a rocket zooms up into the sky, gets further and further away, and then a huge bang and it explodes in millions of tiny red and orange pieces. It seems to last for ever but eventually the fragments disappear. 'Shall we have another one?' I hear Dad shouting. 'Yes, yes,' I jump up and down excitedly. This time, I know exactly what's going to happen, and the anticipation only makes it more magical. I can savour every bit. I can't breathe very well through my nose, so I gawp open mouthed, my face raised up to the sky.

After the rockets come the Catherine wheels. Dad has pinned them to the fence. He lights two at once and then stands back, his smiling face now lit up by the bonfire. To start with, it's just two little matchsticks of fire. But then the whole circles are alight and start whizzing round, screaming as they turn. When they have exhausted themselves, I am given a sparkler to hold and told to keep my gloves on so it can't burn me. The sparks start flying everywhere. 'Wave it around,' Mum shouts. I make zig zag lines, then great big circles. Everyone is smiling. The glow on the stick works its way up towards my gloved hand and just when I start to worry about it setting fire to me, it stops and goes out.

Dad shines the torch in the fireworks box, just to make sure it's empty. The bonfire flames are more subdued now. I hope no one has seen me yawn. I never want tonight to end.

Not long afterwards, I hear various conversations about my mum being in 'the family way again'. When my dad tells my Grandma Farmer about the third baby in four years, she is horrified, 'Yer need to think on. It's no picnic, yer know, 'aving babies, so don't thou go thinkin' it is. 'Ain't yer got enough on yer hands already?'

Cabbage (*Brassica oleracea*)

Before the new baby arrives, we have a big treat. We go out for tea after we've been shopping one Saturday afternoon.

Tips box at Steele's fish and chip restaurant in Grimsby

There's not been a whiff of a tip for several of hours. A family comes in laden with shopping bags and provides a welcome distraction. A nice couple, with their two little girls. She is heavily pregnant with the third one. They look young to have all those children. The girls' eyes are like saucers when they see the tables with white cloths and waitresses bustling about everywhere. 'You do take children, don't you?' the dad asks. 'Yes, as long as they are well behaved,' the waitress says.

It's one of those raw Grimsby days when the east wind blows in from the North Sea. Both girls are in their Sunday best double-breasted coats, the eldest in blue and the youngest in grey. They have little white ankle socks and matching shoes with buckles. They looked half frozen. The eldest looks nervously towards the floor. Big blue eyes, short hair. Takes her coat off, like she's told. The youngest is never still. Dances around. She has an impish look about her.

The mum is dressed up to the nines, a bit of a looker with her hair combed up. Not much over five feet tall, she has the shortest dress and coat on. He is wearing a jacket and tie. A handsome chap right enough. Must be well over 6 feet tall. He might be the sort to leave something at the end for the waitresses. Fingers crossed.

It is lovely and warm inside the restaurant. My fingers, red and cold from all the walking around in the cold, are starting to tingle. A waitress comes over and shows us to a table. She has big hair like Mum's but not as beautiful. She takes her little notepad and pencil out of her pocket, looks at Dad and asks if we have all decided. 'I think so. Fish and chips twice please, a pot of tea and two slices of white bread and butter.' 'And what will the girls have?' she asks over our heads. Mum tells Dad that she thinks a half portion each of fish and a few chips is best and he orders for us.

The food is lovely. After I've finished every last morsel, I place my knife and fork together on the empty plate just the way I have been shown. I say thank you as my plate is taken away and then my sister copies me. Dad nods and says, 'Good girls.' Dad asks for the bill and takes out his wallet. He puts a note on the little dish. The waitress takes the dish away and returns with the change. Dad says, 'That's for you,' and he and Mum agree that she is a nice lady.

When Mum goes into hospital, Grandma Mitchell comes to look after us for a few days. We keep looking out of the lounge window for Dad's car. Our new baby brother is coming home today. Grandma's hair is thick, wavy, and always the same. Not like Mum's hairdos which change every time she goes to the hairdressers. Eventually the tiny white bundle comes home. I can just about see the top of his head above the blanket. He looks like any other baby. He has no hair and a wrinkled face and sleeps in his cot in the room with the orange sloping wall. We must play quietly around him, so as not to wake him up.

I go into hospital to have my adenoids out. I'm told I will feel a lot better when it is all done and that I must be brave.

Cabbage (*Brassica oleracea*)

Mum and Dad take me to hospital, and I clutch my teddy. I don't realise they are going to leave me there by myself and I scream the place down when they go. Mum looks like she is going to cry too. The nurses tell her I will be fine, that they will look after me, and not to worry.

The smell of disinfectant makes me feel sick. I am terrified. I cry and cry. I don't understand why I have been left alone. The nurses tell me 'I must act like a big girl' and that my parents won't be allowed to visit me anymore if I don't behave. There is nothing familiar here apart from my teddy. I hide it under the bedclothes in case that too gets taken away from me as a punishment. I can't eat anything because I am so upset. This makes everyone even crosser. At night I can't settle down to go to sleep and become agitated.

The nurses in uniforms are all looking down at me in my bed, which has railings up on either side. There are bright lights above their faces. They are telling me to be quiet and to stop crying because I will disturb the other patients. I try to get out of my bed and they push me back down. They bring some bandages and tie my hands to the railings at the side so I can't move. Matron is summonsed to calm me down. Eventually they give me something to make me go to sleep. I've never liked hospitals ever since.

I start school when I am five and a bit. I am settling in nicely, becoming less shy every day. At home, we are all getting to grips with this new-fangled ITA Early Reading system written by the same man who invented the shorthand Mum learnt at secretarial school. Dad says it is a fad. Mum says she cannot make head nor tale of it, and even if I manage to learn this, how am I ever going to be able to read regular books? And for sure I will find writing and spelling more difficult as a result.

Playtime after lunch is my favourite bit of the day. We have a massive climbing frame in the playground. And some bars that we can swing on. When the bell rings at the end of it, we must come off any equipment, or stop running and stand quite still. Only then can we go back into the classroom.

Today I am worried I won't get any playtime. The dinner lady in the school hall where we eat lunch, is standing over me, 'Why haven't you finished your pudding?' I explain that I can't eat with a spoon in my right hand, like she is telling me to. Because I'm left-handed. She tells me not to be silly, 'It's good manners to eat pudding with the spoon in your right hand. Now just stop making a fuss and get it eaten. There's no playtime until it's gone, every morsel mind.'

I don't even like currant tart, and the custard is cold and lumpy. I use my left hand to put the spoon in my right hand. I try to cut some of the tart, but I can't get it to work properly. The dinner lady is coming back, and she has that look on her face that tells me I'm in trouble. 'Now come on, I've had enough of this nonsense. What is the matter with you?' I start to cry. This makes her even crosser. I am now the last child in the dinner hall, sitting at the hexagonal table on my little chair. 'I feel sick,' I say.

'Well, that's come on suddenly. If you're that sick young lady, I'll get the office to phone your mum to come and take you home.' Her mouth, with its hairy upper lip, is really close to my head. I wince and put my hand on my stomach for dramatic impact. The school secretary tells me to wait on a chair outside her office until my mother comes, which she duly does, looks at me intently, and takes me home.

When we get through the front door, I make for my sack with all my things in it. A chance to play without being disturbed. Mum shakes her head. 'Oh no young lady. If you think you're going to play with your toys, you've got another thing coming. Now, straight to bed and you stay there until you're better.' I lie on my bed and think of all the others enjoying playtime. After about an hour, she comes up, 'You don't seem that ill to me. What is this all about?' I pour out the whole sorry tale about the dinner lady with the hairy upper lip and how she shouted at me. 'Right. Just wait until your father gets to hear of this. I have never heard such stuff and nonsense.'

As the eldest, I am often in charge. And sometimes I get into trouble if something happens, even when it has nothing to do with me. My little brother is two and a bit and has a patch over one eye to correct his squint. Mum and Dad are playing tennis the other side of the playing fields and we have been sent to play on the swings. He gets on the climbing frame and I am standing at the bottom in case he slips and falls. My sister is on a swing and asks me to push her. The other kids stare at my brother and his patch. 'Spastic, freak,' they shout. My brother is unconcerned and carries on up towards the top. My sister looks at me as if to say, 'Do something. They can't speak to him like that.' In truth they are older and much bigger than me, so my options for fighting back are limited. 'Come on,' I shout up to my brother and then

I say to my sister, 'Let's go back to Mum and Dad.'

We run across the playing fields to the tennis club, where my parents are playing a game of doubles. My dad puts his hand up to the person serving, the game stops and he comes over. We look at him through the wire fence around the court. 'Whatever is the matter?' he asks. 'It's those children, they are saying unkind things about the patch,' I cry. 'Is that all?' he says, 'I thought something serious had happened.' And he goes back to the back of the court to receive the serve.

Whilst still at primary school, I learn not to repeat anything unless you know what it means. But I learn it the hard way.

Mrs Parker's budgerigars' shed in Humberston

The poor little girl is distraught. Mrs P was stomping around earlier, proper furious she was, like red in the face. Even she feels sorry for her now. Her dad is standing behind her. He had a face like thunder before, but he's calmed down too. 'I'm very very sorry,' the girl manages to get out through her sobbing. 'It's all over with now,' Mrs P says to her. 'And I'm sure you've learnt your lesson. Now what do you think of my budgerigars?'

My friend Jane Carr is a few years older than me and knows some bad words. She lives along the road. One day we collect her in Dad's car to come for a play and tea. Dad pops in to see Auntie Lorna and Uncle Fred on the way back home. He says he won't be long and leaves us in the back of the car. The lady in the house opposite is in her garden doing some weeding. We are chatting away, when Jane says, 'Let's wind the car window down and shout at her.'

Because she is older, I don't argue. And she is laughing, so it sounds fun. We find the lever on the car door and lower the window. Then we crouch down low, so she can't see us. On the count of three, Jane says we must spring up and shout 'Fuck off' at the tops of our voices. It's a great game. But after we've done it, the lady's eyes look like they are going to pop out of her head. 'Just wait until your father comes back,' she fumes. I see Dad coming, waving to Uncle Fred and saying, 'See you later.' Like watching a bad car crash about to happen, the lady tells my dad what we said. I have never seen him so cross. His face is like thunder and he says something to the lady. When he gets into the car, he tells me he cannot even speak to me because he is so furious.

Jane gets dropped off. And when we get home, he tells me to get out of his sight. I cannot think of anywhere to go, so I hide behind the sofa. Eventually he comes and tells me to stand in front of him. In a quiet voice, he gives me the biggest telling off and tells me how disappointed he is in me.

I am taken back to the lady's house to say how sorry I am. I can barely get the words out because I am so ashamed. The lady takes me to see her budgerigars. They are blue and yellow and smelly, but I say how much I like them and thank her very much for showing them to me. Both she and Dad are smiling, even laughing now. I'm very relieved when Dad says it's time to go home.

When I am seven years old, I'm told we are going to move to a new place because Dad has got a different job. I am taken to see my new school before the term begins. I meet my teacher and see my classroom, the playground and the playing fields next to the school. We look at the house we will be living in from the outside as people are still living there. Mum and Dad ask me whether I like what I have seen. I have only one concern. I ask whether there will be a garden and if we will still be able to have bonfire nights in the new house. 'Of course,' Dad says.

CHAPTER 5

Carrot (*Daucus carota*)

1981–1984

My interview with the slipper wearing ancient don almost certainly lacks intellectual penetration on my part, but I get an offer to go to King's College, Cambridge, nonetheless. I am gobsmacked and a little scared. Although top dog in my very small grammar school, I am not widely read and certainly not a thinker as I would define it anyway. I am consistently conscientious, focused and don't have a lot else going on in my life, all qualities needed to pass exams.

I am a kind of state school wild card. I decide to chance my arm and apply at the very time they set on a course to increase their non-public school quota. My philosophy at the time is more 'if you can, you might as well try', rather than 'just because you can, you don't have to'. I know it will please my teachers and my parents if I am successful and, in truth, I don't really think about what it will be like to go to Oxbridge and, most importantly, whether I will like it.

Dad tells me the news over the phone, having opened my results envelope. I hear Mum in the background. 'She's got the grades she needed! I don't believe it. Well, she has deserved it. No one has worked harder. Do you think she'll be alright there, mixing with all those kids from posh schools? Now that'll be something else for me to worry myself about. I'm think I'm going to have a sherry.'

I forget about the Pandora's box I have opened. To get my German, which I learnt from scratch in two years up to the level required, I take a gap year before gap years are the norm. But then the day comes, new duvet, mugs and kettle all neatly packed in the boot of my dad's car and we're off. We see King's College Chapel across The Backs as we approach.

Carrot (*Daucus carota*)

Dad is business-like. He helps me carry my worldly goods up the stairs to my room, Number Nine, Market Hostel, and puts my books on the shelves. Then he looks at his watch and says he must go as he has a long drive back, and leaves.

I am invited up to someone's room to meet a few fellow course mates. There are half a dozen of them sitting around in a semi-circle, all incredibly posh. They are speaking loudly and theatrically. One is wearing dungarees, a stripey T-shirt with holes in it and an Indian scarf draped over her shoulders. Another has purple hair, an orange mohair jumper and big hoop earrings. The one sitting next to me has a PVC black miniskirt, fishnet tights, purple lipstick and Doc Martins. My jeans, shirt and home-knitted jumper all feel rather square and ordinary.

'Would you like Earl Grey or regular builders?' one of them says to me. I mumble that I'd like an ordinary tea, please. I'm handed one whilst they all discuss what they have been doing in the summer. Conservation projects in animal orphanages in Asia; travelling overland through eastern Europe in a clapped out mini; digging for archaeological remains in remote Peru. I don't even know where some of the places are that they mention.

The conversation turns to Goethe and the Sturm und Drang movement. And how Schiller is a better example of emerging Weimar Classicism. I am perspiring. I have read my A-level set books and a few other handpicked texts. It seems that they have devoured the entire syllabus even before starting the course. They are so full of their own self-confidence that they do not notice I haven't uttered a single thing.

My introduction to tutorials is no less comfortable. We sit in the professor's office having read two texts and written an essay. I'm above averagely pleased with what I have produced. She looks at me quizzically and says over her spectacles, 'Just to be clear with you, I am not at all interested in your views on Thomas Mann. What I want is a demonstration that you have read and given careful intellectual consideration to the critical sources and insights on the subject. That is how you will do well here.'

An early encounter with the French professor is even more traumatic. 'You failed to pick up the obvious symbolism of Madame Bovary meeting her lover at Trouville,' he ridiculed. When I still look blank, he spells it out. 'Come on, surely you're not that naïve? Trou means 'hole'. The sexual pun is clear for anyone to see.' The adrenaline released through my embarrassment causes me to blush, and I am reminded of the incident on 'the Boneshaker' all those years ago, when I felt similarly humiliated.

In the language tutorial, when we start to chat in German, my spirits rise. At least I will impress now, having spent a year immersed in it. 'Your accent is horrible,' the German Head of Studies says. 'We want Hochdeutsch [high German] not Schwäbisch [local dialect in South Germany].' My dejection is at least short lived since I realise the course will not demand that I speak any German at all. All I must do is become expert in its literature between the sixteenth and twentieth centuries.

My usual formula of applying unlimited industry to any setback is in part successful. In truth, I learn how to do what

Carrot (*Daucus carota*)

is needed, but there is little joy in learning how to do something well and rigorously that you would rather not be doing at all. I quickly conclude that my best strategy is damage limitation. I choose papers where I judge there will be rather more teaching input than supercilious academic point scoring on the part of the tutors. I learn to game the system and graduate three years later with an extremely hard earnt upper second, which my tutor, supportive and affirming to the end, tells me I get by the skin of my teeth.

Though my academic journey is not without difficulty, everything else about being a student suits me very well. I meet this bloke. By reputation, he's often found asleep in the library. 'Well, economics textbooks are so boring, you can't blame me,' he pleads. I first see him next to the pinball machine. He is wearing an oversized khaki great coat from the army surplus stores, white disco boots, round John Lennon rimmed glasses, shaggy thick brown hair, and the navy sweater his grandparents brought back from Guernsey for him. He has braided wrist bands and bangles from his summer of unrequited love in Greece and an earring in his left ear. He is quite the most beautiful man I have ever seen. Olive skinned. The bone structure of a Greek god. A shy but big smile. Focused and in his own little world one minute, and then he turns to face me and it's like the sun has come out.

He trudges round the bar after dinner trying to drum up players for his football team. Most King's men are more into their beer, books and illicit substances than football so it's a thankless task. I catch sight of him cycling up towards the lecture theatres, his white boots standing out from an otherwise brown silhouette. He disappears into the tangle of bikes, bags and people. On one of the changeovers between lectures, we bump into each other. He recognises me as one of the new students at college and he asks me, 'Are you going to the Cellar Bar tonight? There's a freshers' do there. Free booze.'

By one o'clock in the morning when it closes, there are beads of sweat dripping from the ceiling as we jump up and down to the Human League, Madonna, Soft Cell, Eurythmics, and David Bowie. At the freshers' do, having failed to chat up my rather more streetwise friend Rachel, he turns to me. 'And what about you? Sorry I didn't catch your name. What are you studying? Where do you come from? Which kind of school did you go to?' I have not been preparing to meet the love of my life and suddenly my academic challenges pale into insignificance.

The college dining room

An august setting. Ornately carved lofty ceilings. A gallery at one end reached by hidden stairs where the college choir sings at formal occasions. There is wood everywhere. An oak floor and only pictures of founders interrupt the heavily panelled walls. Light is provided by a few low-hanging electric pendants which cast a subdued glow over the long refectory tables with chairs tucked neatly underneath them. It is grand, cold and echoey. Students still in their outdoor coats file into the dining hall from the cafeteria serving area with their metal trays loaded with food. They scour the gloomy space looking for friends to join or choose an unoccupied place where they arrange their plates in front of them and wait for others who are behind them in the queue. Battered metal jugs of water are the only table decoration.

On high days and holidays, we are transformed by flickering lights from huge silver candelabras brought up from the locked stores in the cellars. There is silver cutlery, china and fine wines decanted by the college sommelier. We look forward to the finery and the sense of occasion. It's a shame that students here aren't required to wear gowns to formal hall unlike in the other colleges. It was voted out by the Student Union several years ago and there would be a riot if it were re-introduced. They are required to listen to a few speeches from various college elders, but the main purpose of being here is to neck down as much food and drink as they can for the extra few quid they have to pay on top of the price of normal hall.

Today is a bog-standard cafeteria service. Everyone is accustomed to the unusual eating conventions of the Oxfam-clad handsome student sitting at one of the long trestle tables. Head down over his dented metal tray, he picks up his spoon and finishes his plate of Manchester tart and custard almost before he starts it. Only then does he start on the plate of cottage pie and vegetables which he also clears in record time.

Then he leans back and starts to discuss the politics of the day. 'Bloody Thatcher. Have you seen the article in The Guardian today? The sinking of the Belgrano is an outrage. No justification whatsoever and over 300 people killed. She and her cronies should be held accountable. Why do they get away with it?' And off he goes on one of his diatribes. We hear a lot of political posturing in here from students who think they know it all. We just roll our eyes and let them get on with it.

On Tuesday evenings, we go to the Student Union meeting. I find it fascinating to see how strongly people feel about things. I listen intently and learn a lot. The motion is that we, King's College Student Union, condemn the unlawful imprisonment of Nelson Mandela and demand his immediate release. Passed unanimously. The President is mandated to write to the South African government without delay. We debate the forthcoming rent strike and whether we should occupy buildings. No clear decision. Carried forward for further discussion at next week's meeting. Afterwards people file out into the bar or head into the TV room next door.

One term in and we are officially an item. We hang around together, but we each keep our sets of friends which gradually conflate into one larger group. In the evenings, we have dinner and then check for messages in our pigeonholes in the central mail room. Then we sit in one of the semi-circular booths in the college bar and drink hot chocolate served by the redoubtable and diminutive Dolly who takes no prisoners as she goes about her duties.

The chat ranges from the sublime to the ridiculous and back again. From Structuralism and Marxism to organising sports teams to planning themed parties, pub crawls and what's on *Top of the Pops*. There are some super bright, highly articulate people who hold forth on multiple topics. There are also some very ordinary folk who come from backgrounds not dissimilar to my own. I listen and learn. I have yet to realise that supreme confidence can hide doubt and insecurity and that those with seemingly less to say are often the ones most worth listening to.

Carrot (*Daucus carota*)

Cleaner in Market Hostel

I'm Welsh and Presbyterian, see, so I don't like the thought of all of this smutty living and carrying on. But I need the money, so I spend my weeks cleaning up after the students. They call us bedders. We insist on getting into their rooms at least twice a week. It's not just the sex. Truthfully, student habits are disgusting, so they are. I bet they don't behave like this at home, so why do it here? There are all these lefties at King's. Maybe at the other colleges there's a bit more decency and respect. Mouldy milk left to fester in the corner. Empty bottles used to pee into when they can't be bothered to go down the corridor to the loo in the middle of the night. A sink blocked with vomit. Nail varnish and hair dye all over the bedspreads. Dirty clothes and smelly socks left to gather dust on the floor. We know who has who in their rooms overnight and we certainly need our Marigold gloves when it comes to taking the sheets off the beds.

Why can't they all be like that nice girl in the tweed skirts and lambswool twinsets? She always looks so pretty and has lots of male admirers. Always got flowers in her room and cards. But she has the right idea. Sheets always pristine. She doesn't succumb. A good Christian girl she is. Not like her in Number Nine. She certainly has that boyfriend of hers to stay regularly. How they get any sleep the two of them in that single bed beats me. I've seen him skulking out in the morning. Mind you, it does always seem to be the same one, which can't be said for all of them on this corridor.

The time comes to get acquainted with the parents. He comes from North London, a place I imagine to be teaming with theatre going, artistic, left-wing intellectuals. I wish I am a writer's daughter or a politician's granddaughter, which would bring an instant acceptance and understanding of my back story. I admit to his dad and new partner, 'Sorry, I don't like olives and I've never been to a ballet.' Their house just off Golders Hill Park has original modern art on all its walls and is swathed in tasteful shades of grey and blue. Heal's statement pieces of furniture adorn the sitting room which looks out onto a small but artistically curated patio garden.

His mum and stepdad cook up exotic meals in their trendy West Hampstead basement flat, go out to Chinese restaurants and drink wine out of bottles with corks not demijohns. There are wooden sculptures and textiles collected from their various long-haul adventures in all the rooms, even the bathroom. There is a large courtyard to the rear where we sit and have gin and tonics before dinner. His sister is clever, cool and trendy. Just come back from VSO in Kenya. His brother is quick witted and mixes with musicians. Not for the first time I feel like the country cousin. How different my rural upbringing near the seaside was.

I have forewarned my mum that my love interest has an earring. He believes it marks him out as being 'right on', very avant-garde, though he must take it out when he works in the Beds Department at Selfridges in the summer holidays. Mum is 'highly amused' and says, 'Well this is going to be interesting. Your dad has such a thing about men wearing earrings. Oh, I think that's just hilarious. He won't be able to take his eyes off it.' Everyone is agog, and when they finally meet him, Mum admits, 'I didn't even notice it,' and is disappointed in herself for not being more observant. 'Well, I did,' my dad says pointedly.

Carrot (*Daucus carota*)

It's the end of the first year at university. I have a holiday job at a campsite in south-west France. The summer passes quickly and I become expert at everything to do with putting up and taking down tents. We cart camping equipment around in a rickety trailer attached to our bikes and give advice to customers on which activities lend themselves to an unseasonable amount of rain. Evenings are spent happily in the campsite bar with staff from other companies on site and the 'animateurs' who organise fun activities for children. Occasionally I borrow the campsite moped. I am completely ill-equipped to drive it but venture dangerously into the nearest town to send lengthy airmail letters to various post restante addresses across India where my boyfriend is travelling. I return to the UK with money in my bank account, vowing to do something more adventurous next summer.

Cranmer Road house

I am a large, detached Edwardian gaff without any mod cons. Central heating is for wimps. Ice on the insides of the windows in winter. I am arranged on three floors, attic rooms at the top and what were bedrooms and day rooms on the other two. The garden to the rear was once beautiful but has had scant attention paid to it ever since the college bought me from the previous owners several years ago. Now I'm home to ten second year students. They've got into the whole student vibe by now and don't have the pressure of finals this year, so this place tends to be party central.

Usually, it's group of friends that live together here. This time we've got a lively crowd. Most of them are from the North. They make cushion covers to brighten up the second-hand furniture, put throws bought whilst on exotic holidays over the beds, and buy pot plants from the market stall, which usually don't make it beyond the end of term. True to form, they're planning their first party. It's going to be messy alright.

One of them makes some carrot soup. It's left up in the kitchen on the top floor. There's bread as well, so people can have something to mop up the booze. It's carnage by the end, bodies all over the place. Fag ends on every surface, empty bottles. The stench of sweaty bodies and alcohol. Desperate for more drink, they go round hoovering up the remnants from discarded glasses. Eventually the neighbours complain, and the music must go off. Someone has vomited into the carrot soup pan. Then one of the party goers staggers drunkenly into the kitchen, mistakes it for the real thing and helps themselves to a nice big portion of the orange liquid.

On Valentine's Day in the winter term of the second year, my rather posh former neighbour makes a great thing of borrowing the porters' lodge cart to carry all the cards and floral tributes she has been sent from the post room. Clad in her pink twinset and beige tartan skirt, she crosses the college grounds and needs help to negotiate the raised step at the main entrance. I meet her as I am coming into college. 'I can't believe I've got so many cards and beautiful flowers. I don't know where I will put them all,' she laments and asks me what gifts I have received.

Suddenly, having not been remotely bothered about what day it is, and still less about what it signifies, I decide that it would after all be nice to receive a Valentine's card. I'm not even sure why I have this change of heart, save that I have witnessed someone who has received a disproportionate number and surely to want just one solitary card is only reasonable. When I mention this, I get the predictable response 'that all this hearts and flowers nonsense on one day of the year is pure commercial tokenism and wasn't this what I had always thought as well?' I explain that some things are not a matter of logic, and that it's the thought that counts. Later that day, I am duly presented with a small, dried bunch of flowers from Oxfam (with a 'reduced' price tag on them) and I try to remember those words I spoke a few hours earlier.

Cranmer Road house

The boyfriend of one of the students buys a hat at the vintage stall on the market. It is his constant companion. A trilby with a band around it. He wears it even inside. He looks at himself in mirrors to check just how on trend he is. On a whim, she hides it, his girlfriend I mean. It feels like a risky place to put it, but who are we to say? She and her friend are cooking dinner for everyone. Not the most sophisticated affair we have ever witnessed, but they're having a laugh alright. They hack the frozen budget mince from Fine Fare into manageable pieces and put it into the frying pan to thaw. What a smell it makes as the oil overheats.

Then they make the cottage pie and put the oven on to get warm whilst they set the table next door. She's forgotten, we thought she would, that that's where she has hidden the hat. Luckily our smoke alarm has new batteries. One of the other students shouts, 'There's smoke coming out of the oven!' opens its door and takes out the contents. All hell breaks loose. She leaps up faster than Carl Lewis out of the starting blocks. She knows she is in big trouble and races to the kitchen. Meanwhile others have arrived. They are killing themselves laughing. He has heard the kafuffle and is about to arrive. She can't look at him as he is presented with a perfect miniature charred version of his hat which wouldn't look amiss in a dolls' house.

We are both on the organising committee for the college May Ball. It's the first of many things we will be involved organising together, and indisputably the most disastrous. He oversees marquees. I oversee ticketing. Lots of our close mates are also on the committee. We have a huge boost when The Stranglers agree to be the headline act. But this is followed by a massive worry about potential gate crashers.

The head porter says he is on the case. The Stranglers' pantechnicon drives straight through the porters' lodge and across the hallowed green turf next to the chapel, knocking over the 'DO NOT WALK ON THE COLLEGE LAWNS' sign as it goes. Despite the reassurances, hundreds of ticketless people get in and the paying guests watch them quaff their champagne. As reported by *Vanity Fair*, 'The police banned King's May Ball in the 1980s following an incident with the Stranglers, the Cam and a lot of waterlogged students.'

A more relaxing way of passing the summer evenings is to cycle over to Grantchester and have picnics. Or to walk across the diagonals of Parker's Piece to the pub, where we have a leisurely drink. Or we lounge around on the lawn at the back of college drinking Asti Spumante. We are experts at doing extraordinarily little, and thinking we are incredibly busy. Sundays are the worst days. The combination of feeling wretchedly hung over and guilty because we should be doing some college work but are quite unable to do so.

On Sundays, I queue for the one phone booth in college to call home. Generally, I choose not to share how dreadful I am feeling with my parents, because I anticipate the 'mmm, really, well that's rather disappointing', even though they themselves are not averse to 'a jolly good shindig'. I keep the conversation focused on positive news and heavily edit anything too lurid or unwholesome.

In about 30 years' time, we will receive calls from our student boys, kindly checking in with us on Sunday evenings, as there is little else to do. 'Hello Mum,' (very pained voice) 'yeah hungover, got binned last night. Still feel wasted. Been asleep all day.' In case I can't picture the scene sufficiently clearly, I get to see a photo of a pile of sick next to one of their beds thoughtfully taken and posted on Facebook by one of their friends. 'Sorry Mum, he's a dickhead for doing that.'

And so, graduation comes around before we know it. I have never been to evensong or to the world famous Nine Lessons and Carols in the chapel. I haven't even been to a Cambridge Union debate or to any concerts or plays. All of which I will regret in future years. I have never been to the Provost's Garden, until today. That's where the drinks reception is for the graduates and their parents. It's a beautiful day and everyone is full of smiles and hopes for the future. My parents are as proud as punch.

I am sad to leave. I don't pick up a novel for at least ten years, so deep are the scars from the obligatory literary criticism that has dominated my student years. I have no life plan other than to share a house in London with some friends and to get a job. It's 1984 and we're in a recession. So far, I have no firm offer despite writing one hundred application letters. I mess my interview up with British Gas as I can't name the chairman. I apply for a job I see advertised as a trainee loss adjuster. I don't really know what one does, but the position is in London and they want a graduate, and it has prospects. That will do for now.

CHAPTER 6

Courgette (*Cucurbita pepo*)

1987

The delicious anticipation of the forthcoming weekend is my first waking thought. I am fuzzy headed after drinking a bottle of wine in the restaurant last night, but don't feel as bad as I'm almost certainly going to feel tomorrow morning. I lie in bed for a few minutes. It's Friday, no one will be in the office especially early, so there's no rush.

I shower, thinking about the day ahead. I take time selecting the red woollen dress. It will be fine for the office and for wherever we go after work. I find some bright blue tights and a multi-coloured scarf. The property boom has allowed us to sell our maisonette in the red-light district of Finsbury Park for a big profit and we have moved to this house in Tufnell Park. It needs completely refurbishing. We are living midst builders' detritus and dust sheets on every floor. Stephen has left the Civil Service and is commuting to Reading every day. Consultancy brings much longer days for him and we are a bit like ships that pass in the night. I have just been promoted and from next month will be heading up a big team at the recruitment consultancy I work in. Life feels like it is getting a bit more serious. More grown up.

Speaking of being grown up, we got married last year. On November 1st near Holmfirth, West Yorkshire. The day before was like something out of a comedy sketch. Stephen and the best man missed the church rehearsal due to an overly successful stag night followed by a car incident on the motorway. My brother was the stand-in groom. Various members of Stephen's family, used to the streetlights and multiple signposts of London, got totally disorientated on the moors and sent out an SOS to be rescued and guided to their accommodation. And the dressmaker still hadn't quite finished my wedding dress with hours to go. The normal pre-wedding stress.

But the actual day went to plan and was beautiful. A traditional church wedding with the bells in the tower rung before and afterwards. The minister thoughtfully asked us to turn round and face the congregation halfway through the service so that we could see everyone and remember the faces looking at us. I promised to 'honour' not 'obey' and we walked back down the aisle with the choir singing *Jerusalem*. We got into the white Rolls Royce my mum had always dreamt of, then we went to a nice old hotel Mum and Dad had chosen for the reception. There were speeches and lots of laughter. Then an evening 'do' with a disco. Lots of my work friends came up and stayed. We somewhat bizarrely drove back down to London that same night, as we had an early plane the next morning to Marrakech from Gatwick. An accident of annual leave entitlement and plane schedules.

I navigate the stairs, which are covered with plastic, down to the kitchen. Bits of old plaster crunch underneath my feet. It's the end of the month, so I need to get that offer nailed down and on the whiteboard by the end of the day. It will take me over my sales target. And the commission will pay for the new curtains, I think. The Habitat catalogue is on the kitchen table. I'm thinking navy and claret to go with the sofa. We've had the old PVC windows taken out and installed new wooden sash windows that are more in keeping with the Victorian house. The woodchip paper has been removed and the pine floors stripped, leaving gaping gaps between the old boards.

I check the fridge. There's an onion, half a block of cheese and the remains of a pack of butter. It needs cleaning out, I note. No shopping has been done all week. We've run out of bread and milk, so I'll have to leave without any breakfast. I'll pick some up on the way to the office. I remind Stephen I'm out with my work mates tonight and kiss him goodbye. He says he's going to be late back too. I grab my bag and coat and start walking towards the tube station. It's a sunny morning and as I pass the playing fields at the end of the road, I see the public tennis courts and think it would be nice to have a game at the weekend.

I walk up the hill to the tube station. Outside the entrance, I buy a newspaper for the journey and make my way down the steps to the dark tunnel. Margaret Thatcher has just won a third landslide election victory. How outrageous that there is hardly a woman in her cabinet, I reflect. Why is it a lot of female leaders think they must talk and act just like the men around them? The new MD at work is a prime example. Just appointed, she is an imposing woman and clever. She has led successful teams in the business, but everyone is wary of her. She is a force to be reckoned with alright, throws her weight around verbally and can be ruthless. Not a good idea to get on the wrong side of her and if you argue too much with her, your card is marked. Surely there is a way to be tough as well as fair-minded and compassionate?

I think I'll learn a lot from her when I take up my new job, but I'm also nervous that she will expect me to approach things in a certain way and I don't want to end up becoming a mini version of her. Work up until now has been fun. A laugh. And because I've been quite good at it, I've been well paid as well. Oh well, things can't stay the same for ever, I guess. Fridays have always been very relaxed in the office. Maybe that too will change in time. Better enjoy it whilst I can. As I emerge from Blackfriars Station, we file like ants up the escalators to ground level. I get a view of the Thames and go to buy a takeaway coffee and a croissant. After all, it's Friday and I have had a good sales month so I deserve it.

The office is over a post office where there is a regular flasher. There is a grotty lobby with a lift to our first-floor open plan offices which has windows on two sides, a small kitchen and four interview rooms off reception. I go through reception, where Camilla, the twinset and pearled receptionist is fiddling with her flicked back hair. She lives in Kensington in one of Daddy's flats, 'Oh hi there. Glorious outside, isn't it? Just divine. Wouldn't it be marvellous if it were like this the whole weekend? Some chums and I are hoping to have Pimm's and strawberries in the park.'

As I go through to the main open plan office, I see everyone has their heads stuck in a newspaper, and most are smoking. I sit and drink my coffee and enjoy my croissant whilst reading *The Times*. My current manager sitting opposite says, 'Don't rush, it's Friday and the new MD isn't in today,' as I hurry my paper away, thinking I should get on and do something. Two colleagues who work with investment banks are talking intently about a client of theirs with a name that sounds like a packet of breakfast cereals. They are doing a deal in the US according to the *FT*, so they might want to do some lateral hiring and they have a few ideas about some possible candidates.

In about an hour, the owner sweeps in, 'Seems awfully quiet in here. Come on you lot, it's not Friday evening yet. Time to do several deals before we shut up shop.' The huge whiteboard on the wall is almost entirely filled with confirmed fees but he likes to keep us on our toes. Rumour is he is preparing to sell the business. That's why he's appointed the new MD. To 'shake things up' a bit. But it's been a good month and he will treat us all to champagne later. That's how he has always run things, ever since he set up the business. He is generous to his staff when times are good, and the business is making lots of money, which in the booming 1980s is almost a given. I've not been around when things are tougher, but have no doubt that under the new regime things would get pretty uncomfortable if you weren't meeting targets.

I like him, but I'm always on my toes making sure I stay in his good books. He has a lived-in red face, big advertising tortoiseshell glasses and a brown, expensive looking coat. He always has the *FT* under his arm. Woe betide you if you haven't spotted something going on in your sector. 'You need to be on it, not reacting the whole time.' He flicks at the offending page in frustration, 'Wake up. That's what I pay you for.' We watch him in his glass sided office. He is an open book. When he gets annoyed, you hear it before you see it. He rants and raves and thumps the desk. The beads of sweat build on his forehead and tumble down the reddening face. Equally, he has a great sense of humour and fun, and there's a lot of laughter, providing things are going well.

I came here for an interview about two years ago. Most

people had known each other even before they started working here. I quickly learnt everyone is referred to by their initials, or a pre-existing nickname. I was greeted in reception by someone who was at Cambridge at the same time as me. It turns out we had friends in common. In fact, it appeared that half the office was from Oxbridge. Usually, I have very mixed feelings about telling people where I went to university. Something instilled very deeply in me by my parents means I feel it's blowing my own trumpet even to mention it. If I am specifically asked, I am reluctant to reveal this fact for fear I will be judged as 'one of those Oxbridge types', which I don't consider myself to be. Finally, here, it seems it is an advantage and the interview went well. 'It's all very relaxed,' I was told, 'lots of banter and leg pulling.' I came away pretty sure I was going to get the job. And the fit felt good with where I was in my life. A kind of drop-in centre for topflight graduates with no idea what they want to do.

To be honest, it's been a hoot. We work hard and play hard. I feel embarrassed about the fact that recruiting during a City boom is a licence to print money and have earnt more than I ever imagined. Today I've asked my manager for some advice about closing the deal I was thinking about as I was getting ready this morning. Rings of smoke rise above his head as he alternately draws on his cigarette and talks me through the call I'm about to make. The candidate is an accountant, recently qualified, with a job offer to move into stockbroking. My manager leans back and gives me his considered view and advice.

'He should take the job. He would be a complete fucking

idiot if he didn't take the job. He has got a crappy CV, messed up his exams first time, frankly got an unimpressive degree, and this lot are seriously respected brokers. It will set him up for life. Tell him not to be so wet. If he doesn't take it, quite honestly, he is a wanker. You can tell him, he's got me to deal with if he farts about trying to negotiate a better offer. I mean who does he think he is?' He sees my astonished face and laughs.

'With coaching like that, how can I fail?' I say. I take a moment and think what I'm going to say to him in the event I need to give him a bit of a push in the direction of taking the job. I look at my manager, who gives me a 'get on with it' kind of look, pick up the phone and dial. I'm spared having to give the candidate the sales spiel, because he has decided to accept the offer. He's given his notice in and will start next month. I give a thumbs up sign across the desk as I'm talking. I come off the phone and report that it's an early invoice too, which always goes down well.

High fives all round. 'Go and put it on the board, make the boss's day,' my manager says. To celebrate, in my lunch hour, I nip into the Next shop near St. Paul's Cathedral, and quickly flick through the rails of vivid coloured shirts and co-ordinating checked skirts and knitwear. It's my 'go to' place for work clothes. Neither Lady D frilly collars, cardigans and floaty patterned skirts, nor 'f*** off' padded shoulders and great wide belts worn by the City lawyers and bankers. I'll get quite a lot of commission on this month's pay slip, so I feel justified in selecting a couple of items.

On the way back to the office, I peer into restaurants and wine bars. Standing room only. If I pass an open doorway, I hear raucous laughter. No vacant black taxis. Shops teeming with people desperate to spend their money. Cranes reaching up to the top floors of new office accommodation. I buy my takeaway coronation chicken sandwich, a Friday ritual, and take it to eat at my desk. Everyone is reading their papers again. The boss is out to lunch with some City bigwig.

The atmosphere in the office this afternoon is quite subdued, with everyone conserving energy for tonight and the weekend. Someone in the team next to us is having a nap at his desk having had a late night last night. The manager of the Commerce and Industry team is just returning from entertaining one of his biggest clients at El Vinos across the road. He's fuming.

'Bloody hell, she can drink, that woman. Built like a tank. I thought she wanted to have lunch to give me some more business. But no, shit, she wants another bloody job. Thinks Dave her CEO is an arsehole, and they've fallen out basically, so the writing is on the wall. Bugger. She is one of my biggest clients.' He slumps in his chair dejectedly.

The photocopier is whirring in the background. 'Who didn't fill the bloody paper tray after they used it last?' one of the secretaries calls out to no one in particular. 'Shit, it's got jammed. That's all I bloody need on a Friday afternoon.'

Each of the five secretaries, all from Essex way, sit with the team they work for and relations are sometimes tense.

'I am not working for that lot anymore, they're about as much bloody use as an ashtray on a motorbike. I ain't being funny, but they haven't got a clue.' But she has only just got started. 'Bleeding hell, if you think I'm doing that bloody great big mail shot by the end of today, dream on sunshine, cos I ain't. No way, Jose. I'm out of here on the dot tonight, otherwise I won't get a seat on the train.'

The finance manager has a desk and a computer, the only one in the whole office, two floors down in the basement. He looks haggard. He has been summoned by the boss on his return from lunch and comes up clutching reams of paper. Something has gone wrong with the forecasting and not as much invoicing has been done as was expected. He will get the blame. 'What do I bloody pay him for?' the boss can be heard ranting. Dejected, he walks around between the desks, asking each manager if there are any more invoices to be sent out. We've all heard the commotion and want to help him out if we can. But if we give him the nod to invoice a fee ahead of its due date, the clock on the payment terms will start ticking, with more pressure put on us to chase it up, so most people shake their heads as he passes. Eventually he quietly returns, even more subdued, to his lightless basement office and redoes the numbers.

There are piles of envelopes to frank before we all call it a day. 'Oi can some of you lot give us a hand?' screams the secretary across the room. 'Bleeding hell fire, they're all sitting around and I'm working ten to the bleeding dozen over here.'

Meanwhile Camilla in reception asks in her cut-glass accent if we can make sure the diary for next week is up to date. 'It's really jolly embarrassing if someone, you know, comes in and I don't know who they are. Makes me look, you know, rather stupid.'

Eventually, envelopes stuffed, and the secretaries safely departed for their train back to Chingford, the boss says, 'Ok team, great month. I'll go over the road and start getting the drinks in. Switch the lights off before you leave. Don't want them on all bloody weekend.'

And he swoops out, us not far behind him. Fleet Street is emptying for the weekend as we make our way into the wine bar and the boss has already got a couple of bottles of champagne on ice ready and waiting. They are both drained before the last people out of the office get through the door. 'Another couple of bottles please,' the boss says over the growing din. We are now standing shoulder to shoulder and I talk ever more extravagantly with my hands. Every time my glass is jolted by someone trying to get past, it gets filled again, before I can say 'Camden Town'.

I lose track of time and of myself. It's usually the way on a Friday evening. Soon it is 8pm and the effects of two or three hours of fizz are clear. And we all decide we urgently need something to eat. We go outside and hail a taxi. The air is sobering. After a few minutes we have flagged down three taxis and there's shouting between everyone as to where we are all heading. Eventually there's a modicum of agreement. 'Frith Street Soho please,' each taxi driver is told. Someone phones ahead to check availability at a couple of places in the vicinity and eventually we all pile into a Greek restaurant quite close to Tottenham Court Road. It's a cavernous, noisy place on many levels.

We are directed to the basement, two floors away from the nearest ladies' loos. I pop my coat on the back of a chair and follow the signs upstairs. As I am washing my hands, I check in the mirror for visible signs of inebriation. Seeing the reflection of Grandma Farmer's ghost standing behind me is not quite what I had anticipated, and I suddenly sober up. I've been expecting something like this ever since the funeral service last year when Grandma's ghost spoke to me for the first time and concluded by saying, 'Ah'll be seein' thee,' as I sat in the church looking at her coffin. I had thought she might appear at our wedding, but maybe there were too many people around and it wasn't the right vibe for ghost visits.

As Grandma's ghost begins to speak to me in her familiar broad Yorkshire accent, I am taken immediately back to my childhood.

'Well, lassie, ah see yer took mah advice about gettin' hitched. What a reight bonny bride yer made. Ah didn't want to get in way on yer big day, so just kept mysen to mysen. Blimey, this London life is a bit lively ain't it? Ah've ne'er seen such fancy stuff as they serve 'ere. Ah'd love to know what's in them little fried balls ah've seen comin' and goin' on various trays. Ah'm finding out about all sorts o' new stuff these days. Looks like some kind of vegetable in 'em. Yer grandad wouldn't 'ave thanked me for messin' around with 'is vegetables like that. 'Ee liked 'em boiled, or in soup. Anyway, lassy, mek sure yer get thissen 'ome safely. It's gettin' late and ah don't like to think of yer by yerself wandering around these 'ere streets. Yer ne'er know 'oo might be around.'

Taramosalata and humous with pitta bread are already on the table when I get back downstairs. I like the fact that

Courgette (*Cucurbita pepo*)

Grandma hasn't disappeared out of my life. She was always a bit of an enigma when she was alive, so maybe I will get to know her better through her ghost. The waitress arrives with plates of dolmades, stuffed aubergines and moussaka. She puts them in the middle of the long table. I ask her about the little fried balls Grandma was referring to. She says they're just coming. 'What are they made from?' I ask. She is the daughter of the owner, so gives me a full answer.

'You mean the Kolokithokeftedes?' She looks in the direction of another waitress who is bringing two plates of them to the table. 'They're made from zucchini, courgettes. The traditional Greek way is to mix them with feta cheese, oregano, a little flour and add some ouzo for an aniseed flavour. Then we serve them with Greek yoghurt and cucumber and lemons. It's one of my favourite dishes.'

I wonder if Grandma got all of that. Who knows what she hears and what she doesn't these days? As I help myself to a couple of them, the boss is shouting down the table, 'I've booked a couple of tables at Annabel's. Taxis in an hour.' Suddenly the table is so full of food I feel a bit overwhelmed, but I tuck in to get some food inside my stomach to counter the fizz. Everyone is shouting to be heard. The Greek dancers come out, the music gets put up and people start to dance on the table and break plates. Everyone starts banging on the table, 'More, more, more!'

I check my watch. It's now after midnight and I have a twinge of conscience that Stephen might be worried where I am. The boss is paying the bill. 'Come to Annabel's. I've booked a table. It will be fun. We can order some more champagne.' I hear a remaining bit of my sensible self say, 'No thanks, I want to get the last tube, thanks for a great evening and have a good weekend.' I go to Tottenham Court Road and down into the depths of the Northern Line. The illuminated board indicates that there are no more trains. I come back up to street level and stand on Oxford Street. I look in vain for taxis with their yellow lights on. I start walking down towards Warren Street. The quickest way home on foot is familiar because I did it several times whilst the tube strike was on.

I sober up during the two mile walk through the familiar streets of London at nearly one in the morning. It is peaceful with only tramps sleeping in doorways for company. I put some coins in the cup one of them holds out towards me. I follow the same route as the tube line, walking past Camden Town Station and then Kentish Town. Night buses pass me with passengers slumped asleep against the windows. A refuse lorry comes along and the rubbish sacks left out by the side of the road are thrown into the back of it. I pass the playing fields on my left and can see the house a few hundred yards ahead. I hope Stephen is asleep.

The weekend is ahead of me. But first a much-needed lie in.

CHAPTER 7

Kale (*Brassica oleracea*)

1991–1992

Five days overdue, my waters break just as Sue Barker is announcing the final scores on *A Question of Sport*. 'Go and stand in the bath,' my husband says helpfully. It seems as good a plan as any, so I do as he suggests. I remind myself whilst standing there how much I dislike the chocolate brown bathroom suite in this house we've just moved into. I can hear clattering and movement downstairs. Eventually I shout down, 'What are you doing?' He responds, 'I'm just looking for the plant spray.'

When he comes back upstairs, he is clutching it triumphantly and I give him a 'What the heck?' kind of look. 'The midwife said I should take it to the hospital. To spray you when you're in the last stages of labour. It's refreshing and will distract you.' He's also carrying a bag of sandwiches sufficient to feed the entire labour ward. 'We could be there for some time,' he explains, 'need to keep my strength up.' As we are leaving the house, he makes one final dash back inside. 'Just remembered these.' He holds a small stack of CDs aloft. 'There is a music player in the delivery room apparently.'

Mum sends an airmail letter every week, the last one telling me how excited they are to be coming home in a few weeks. I imagine her waiting by the phone in Nairobi for news of her first grandchild. I have eaten my way through the third trimester and imagine the excess will magically disappear once I've given birth. My huge belly meant I had to stop unpacking the removals boxes after I couldn't bend over and reach the bottom anymore. The baby equipment has all been ordered from Mothercare and, for good measure, we have added a frieze of green and lemon teddy bears to the nursery, suitable for a boy or a girl.

In the antenatal classes, we have bathed plastic dolls and simulated labour pains by gripping each other's arms. Models of the pelvic floor were passed around and examined. I have practised my breathing techniques and got my overnight bag packed for 'when it happens'. Penelope Leach's *Baby and Child* sits on my bedside table, well leafed through.

Several injections of pethidine into a long night, I hear classical music as if in some parallel universe. Like in a dream, people appear, check the baby's heartbeat, or feel my stomach and then go out. There are frequent updates on how many centimetres I am dilated. My husband holds my hand. Apparently, some women swear and curse in the labour ward, but I tell him that I love him. Everything seems calm. An additional monitor is put on me. The pains are stronger now, and the simulations in the classes a distant memory. The midwife doesn't leave the room. 'It won't be long now.'

The urgency to push takes me by surprise. He comes out in a rush. After he has swished across the delivery table, 'A boy, you've got a beautiful boy, and he's a big one alright,' the other nurse in the room lifts him on to the weighing scales. 'He's weeing all over the place. At least we know that's all working,' she says. Beyond beautiful with lots of dark brown hair, he is wrapped up tightly in a blanket and has a little cotton hat to keep him warm. I am stitched and we are both checked over, then wheeled back to the ward. He sleeps in a plastic cot next to me, the same height as my bed. I suddenly wonder what on earth will happen when he wakens. I am shown how to breast feed by a very matter of fact nurse. 'It's just like riding a bike.

Once you get into the swing of it, you'll be producing so much milk, you won't know what to do with it. Have you got a pump, so you can put the extra in the freezer?'

Once home, a rather brisk health visitor comes every morning. She has little truck with my teary stories about non-stop feeding and a baby that never seems satisfied. I am allowed a few days grace before she takes in the unmade bed, my dishevelled nighty-clad appearance and the milk-stained baby grow then decides I need taking in hand. She claps her hands together like a schoolteacher who has had enough of an unruly class.

'Right. What we need here is some routine. Once you have given the baby his early morning feed, you put him back in his basket and get yourself up and sorted for the day. Quick shower, get yourself dressed and then straight downstairs to do a hoover round, get some washing on and prepare a nice casserole for when your husband gets home. Have you got one of those slow cookers? Really good they are. I tell all my ladies about them. And so simple to use. You just chop a few onions and carrots, then pop them in the ceramic dish with some diced beef or pork. Or chicken legs are good. Switch it on and you'll have a delicious meal, all ready by tea-time. And make sure you have some nice green vegetables every day. Kale is the best. It's good for breast feeding baby. Lots of calcium and iron as well as vitamins. You can get it on Altrincham Market, a great big bag full for a few pence. Right, I'll see you tomorrow. Hopefully, you'll be dressed by the time I get here.'

And she sweeps out of the room and clomps down the stairs. 'I am a capable person,' I remind myself, 'who managed to hold down a responsible job before I had a baby.' I hear her taking her coat off the bannister, then there are a few moments delay. Now she is walking briskly in her sensible shoes to the front door. I just want her gone. When I hear the door slam, another casualty of her heavy handedness, I grab a bit of the duvet, as a child would a comfort blanket, bury my head in it and cry.

The ghost of Grandma

'Well, that were a reight carry on, werent' it? Thou tek no notice of 'er. What a reight bossy cow she is. 'Oo does she think she is, bossin' mah granddaughter around like that? It'll just tek a bit of time to get thissen a routine. It's no picnic 'aving a baby, it ain't. And she needs to think on 'ow she speaks to folk. Yer need some rest lassy. Thou looks done in. Now, the baby's fast on, so why don't yer get thissen a bit o' shuteye, whilst thou can. Yer'll 'ear 'im reight enough if he wakens.'

Perhaps hearing how the health visitor went on brought back bad memories for Grandma. Mum told me lots of stories about how Grandma had to put up with living in the same house as the woman who used to be known as Nanna, my dad's grandmother. Nanna's constant bossiness and criticisms over the years undermined my grandma and wore her down. But there was no way out of the situation because of the coal allowance that Nanna got after her husband died. He was a miner down the pit and the weekly pile of coal dumped on the street outside the house was the only pension she received and provided heat for the whole family. I check the baby again, then pull the covers over my head and fall into a deep sleep.

Four months on, she is taking the celebration sponge cake out of its box. Not being religious, they decide on a welcoming party instead of a christening. It has 'Welcome Matthew' written on it in chocolate letters. She arranges the last of the sausage rolls on a plate, then places them in the middle of the buffet. She is wearing a bright red dress and has had her hair blow dried at the hairdressers. The baby and life in suburban Altrincham have found contentment in their respective routines.

At first, this place felt too perfect after the disorder and bustle of North London. No run-down houses, derelict buildings, or graffiti on walls. Instead, newly painted exteriors and front doorknobs polished, beautifully landscaped gardens, every streetlight working and even the centres of roundabouts planted with care. To begin with, they knew no one. They rented a small house and lived in between sharp-suited Mike, the man from Kellogg's whose job it was to invent new cereals, and Winifred, conservative with a small and large 'C' who had a flagpole in her tiny front garden and flew the Union Jack on royal birthdays.

Whilst heavily pregnant, she met other expectant mothers at NCT coffee mornings. What a culture shock that was. Sitting around in circles discussing the whys and wherefores of muslin squares or nursing bras felt so alien to her. After all, she had been used to operating in the cut and thrust male-dominated world of recruitment. The rhetoric on breast feeding was overwhelming and the unspoken 'how to be a perfect vegan' competition that existed amongst some members of the group was comical. However, this was more than compensated for by meeting two kindred souls with whom she would share this new journey called motherhood.

The old house in Tufnell Park was eventually sold and the familiar furniture, whose existence she had almost forgotten, was unloaded from the removals van and carried up the steps into the narrow terrace house close to the town centre. Only last week was the last cardboard box finally unpacked.

The welcoming party takes place on Saturday afternoon on the weekend before she goes back to work. She has a new job that she was interviewed for only a few weeks ago. The house is full of a new kind of chaos. Recently bathed, freshly changed babies are lined up on the floor in their car seats. Adults tower above them and chat. They go backwards and forwards to the kitchen to recharge their glasses, checking the floor as they go for discarded baby toys and more babies lying on changing mats in unexpected places. When people get hungry, they crowd round the dining room table, which has been pushed back against the wall, and fill their paper plates full of quiche, sandwiches, crisps and vol au vents. There's a speech and a toast to the health of the new baby. Everyone can see that their new life in Manchester is suiting them well. She is smiling and looks radiant. 'Life is so good, I almost think it can't stay this way,' she is heard to say.

Her brother taps her on the shoulder and says he must go now, to catch his flight back to Brussels. As often happens at parties, she feels they have not had chance for a proper catch up. 'Great do,' he says, 'I can see this baby has properly taken over the show. I'll be coming back in a few weeks with work, and we can have a long chat then.' She follows him as he goes to find his coat and bag. They say goodbye and she hugs him for the last time, then watches him hurry down the narrow hallway. He's always in a rush. She hears him cracking a joke with her sister about opening a rival to Mothercare, such is the amount of baby paraphernalia in the house. He opens the door, then is gone. She returns to the party, which shows no sign of finishing any time soon.

Two months after the welcoming party, I wake at 5.30am, as I hear the baby stirring next door. The sun is shining through the blinds. I pull back the duvet from my side of the bed and tiptoe out of the room down the corridor. I put my head round the door of the nursery. He is sitting contentedly in his cot, his face still bleary from sleep. He smiles when he sees me and waves his arms excitedly. Those huge blue eyes. I instantly forgive him for waking up so early.

The first morning after my maternity leave finished, I drove to the nursery and waited for the door to be opened by the smiley owner at 8.00am. I handed him over to the nursery nurse and she reassured me he would be fine. I cried all the way to my new office, five miles away. I looked in the rear-view mirror and tidied myself up before taking the stairs up to the reception area. The baby loved it from the very first day. Always something going on. I'm the one who has struggled. I had not anticipated such a fierce and strong maternal bond with this little being who has turned our lives upside down. And work is tough going. It's an established recruitment firm, but the market is still in recession. As the only working mum in the office, I feel I have to run twice as fast as the blokes to show how committed I am.

Kale (*Brassica oleracea*)

I pick him up out of his cot and smell his nappy. Yuk, that's why he woke up. I pop him on his changing mat and strip off his baby grow before changing him.

Now he thinks it's playtime, and no amount of peekaboo games or raspberry noises on his tummy is enough. We go downstairs together and I warm up his bottle. I strap him in his little rocking chair so I can get some washing on and empty the dishwasher whilst I'm waiting for the microwave to ping.

I give him his warm milk. And I breathe in his delicious smell before I take him back upstairs and lay him on a towel on the bathroom floor. He gurgles and kicks his legs as I quickly shower. Gone is the luxury of standing under the hot spray for ages, contemplating life. I dry myself, wrap a towel around me and take him into his room to dress him, then I fill the changing bag with more nappies and baby wipes. I go back into our bedroom and hand him to his dad who is just awake. 'Remember you're taking him to nursery this morning. I've given him his milk and sorted the bag for nursery. But he still needs to have his porridge.'

I have an early client meeting for a new assignment and a 7.00am rendezvous with my boss near Junction 7 off the M56. I get dressed then do my prep whilst gobbling down a piece of toast. My shirt is slightly creased. No time to get the iron out, I smooth it with my hands. Yesterday I turned up wearing one navy blue shoe and one black one. At least they were on the correct feet. My boss is ex-army, and his wife doesn't work. 'She's there for our two girls and keeps things ship shape at home,' he explains. Does it ever cross his mind how much easier this makes his life?

I run back upstairs and, whilst I am putting on some mascara, shout from the bathroom, 'There's not much food in the fridge and we're low on nappies. I'll pop into Sainsbury's on the way home.' I run into the bedroom, where the baby is laughing and being jiggled up and down on his dad's raised knees. I kiss them both, rush back downstairs, grab my keys and briefcase and walk quickly to the car. I look at my watch and sigh. I'm late.

He's standing by the driver's side of his car and does a quick time check as I pull up at the appointed place. I hear him clicking his exceedingly shiny shoes together and see him stand up straight and salute. He gets back into his car and opens the passenger door for me. As I'm putting my seatbelt on, he switches off the radio. 'How are we doing this morning?' he says, without being interested in my reply. 'Great,' I say, 'never better.' On the way to the pitch meeting he reminds me that male clients often prefer to work with consultants where they feel there is a meeting of minds.

During the meeting, I am reduced to taking notes because I can't get a word in edgeways. Nor can the client for that matter. My boss goes on and on about the army and discipline, the new BS5750 quality kitemark the firm has been awarded, and our commitment to process and documentation. I stare out of the window at the beautiful morning. Perfect weather for pushing the baby round the park, then meeting my friend for coffee. Afterwards, he doesn't ask me how I think the meeting went. He rather smugly preaches that 'It's all about taking control and giving

Kale (*Brassica oleracea*)

clients confidence in us.'

We drive separately back to the office. By the time we have parked and taken the lift to the first-floor reception, the client we met earlier has already phoned to say we haven't won the job. I sit behind my desk wondering why I am here. I think about the baby at nursery and what he is doing. Financially, it's not an option to walk out. I feel like a fish swimming in someone else's water, the blokes in the office look out for each other but I am not included. Finding my own work when I have no existing contacts will be a lonely old path. Still, I refuse to be beaten, and dealing with that hard-faced MD in my old job taught me resilience, if nothing else.

At lunch time, I go out for some fresh air and to buy a sandwich. I'm still struck by the difference between the gentrified town of Wilmslow, where the office is, and Blackfriars, where I used to work. In front of me is Hoopers, a department store for the seriously well-off, with more designer brands than you can shake a stick at. I choose a tuna and cucumber on granary bread from M & S, which is just next door to the store. It's really warm now, and I take my jacket off and raise my face to the sun. As I walk back to the office, I think back to those crazy nights in the booming 1980s, when we all drank far too much and had such a laugh. Maybe even in London everything is more subdued now. Anyway, these days, I'm so tired by the end of the week, a bowl of pasta and a glass of wine is about as much as I can manage before falling asleep in front of the TV. Life is so different now.

As I eat the sandwich at my desk, I hear the phone ring outside my office and become aware of sudden movement.

The PA, a middle-aged woman with a kind face rushes into my office and, without being able to look at me insists, 'Your husband has just phoned. He and the baby are fine, but you need to go home right now.' I gather my things, pick up my car keys and do as she says. She continues to avoid my gaze as I leave the office. 'I'll call you later,' I say behind me. Stephen rarely calls me during the day. Something bad has happened. I drive the five miles home listening to the radio. I have no idea what I am listening to. I manage to find a parking space right outside the house. I go through the motions of grabbing my briefcase and handbag, locking the car, running up the steps and turning my key in the lock.

She goes through the front door and gets as far as the dining room. The look on her husband's face is frightening. He crumples, unable to be as brave as he had promised himself he would be. He tells her that her brother has been killed. Life as she has known it stops, right there and then. She asks where the baby is, and she goes to get him from his cot. She clings on to him and buries her head in his small body. Nothing makes sense. They need some fresh air. They go for a walk in the park, but the circumstances are so cruelly different than she had been imagining earlier whilst stuck in that meeting. She looks up to the sky, wondering where her brother is. She takes in the flowerbeds with marigolds round the outside and neatly trimmed rose bushes in the centre. Is this what he is now? A part of nature. She worries he is lonely. He always liked company. She is changed for ever. The expression 'it's a chance in a million' will henceforward offer no comfort.

Kale (*Brassica oleracea*)

She recalls that last Christmas, she and he sat up late together in front of the fire. She was doing the last feed before settling the baby down for the night and he kept her company. It was the last time they were alone together. He said he loved living in Brussels and had no plans to return to the UK. He told her about his recent business trip to New York and his visit to the tailor to get two suits made. They laughed together about how he was living life in the fast lane and had become so important and short of time that he needed his own personal dresser. 'Anyway,' he said in his usual matter-of-fact way, 'I'm going to die young. And it will be quick.' She thinks of the last hug she gave him at the welcoming party. If only she had known she would never see him again.

He'd been killed. On the island of Lamu. He'd gone there for a few days from Nairobi, where he was visiting our parents. He died instantly from a massive blow to the back of his head. He had been walking to the beach to take some photographs before catching his flight back to the mainland when it happened. The perpetrator stole his training shoes. Those are the facts. An appropriately random death for this gentle giant to whom random things always seemed to happen. The headline in the *Daily Mail* ran, 'Who killed gentle Jon?' She had been asked for a photo of him for the front-page story. The only one she could find that did justice to his beautiful face was taken at their wedding five years ago. He was standing next to her in her white wedding dress, a carnation in his lapel. She cut herself out of the photo before sending it to the newspaper's Fleet Street offices, near where she used to work in Blackfriars.

She'd never liked Lamu. Two years ago, she and her husband had spent three days on the same island, an original Swahili settlement off the coast of Mombasa. It was a Christmas gift from her parents when they visited them in Kenya. She was excited to go, having read accounts of the unique way of life there in the travel sections of several weekend papers. She can see it now, looking over the pilot's shoulder as they approached the tiny landing strip, trees on both sides. Their luggage was waiting at the bottom of the steps as they disembarked. They walked to the rickety jetty, where a carved out rowing boat and a crowd of men were waiting. The crossing to the main town was unrelaxing. It was so much hotter than it had been in Nairobi, and there was arguing between the two men rowing our boat. There was unfinished business with those left on the jetty who were shouting angrily after us, gesticulating with their fists.

Once they arrived at the town, she was overwhelmed by the noise, the dust and number of people in the narrow streets. Women with water jugs on their heads, men pushing agricultural carts, street sellers, mopeds leaving black clouds of fumes behind them, children playing. A stripped-back existence. Every man for himself. It was humid, airless, and strangely forbidding. It felt edgy.

They explored the old town and then took a walk to the white sanded beach. They stood out, uncomfortably so, from the locals. They got a bit sun burnt and retreated to their dark, basic room where she cut the end of her finger badly on the rotating blade of an ancient fan. A permanent scar of embedded blue metal would gradually fade on her wedding ring finger, unlike her memory of this place.

The following day, they took a fishing trip. They sat on opposite sides of the uncomfortable wooden boat. She could not get out of the piercing sun. She tried to sit away from the coils of rope which unfolded violently when the sails were changed. Suddenly she was aware of a commotion, people bent over the side of the boat, shouting. Then something alive and frantically twitching came on board over the side and landed about two metres away from her.

There was more shouting and sudden movement of bodies towards the flapping fish, unbalancing the boat. Instinctively, she made herself as small as she could and looked the other way. She heard the dull sound of rocks hitting flesh. There was blood and bits of skin everywhere. 'It's dead,' one of them said. The blows stopped and she felt like throwing up. She looked across the boat at her husband for comfort.

The fax machine on the filing cabinet next to her desk starts whirring, spewing out a large document which falls onto the floor. Strange, because she's not expecting anything. She picks up the sheets and puts them in order. It's the post-mortem report on her brother. Reduced to a description of various body parts like in a biology lesson. She reads it but cannot relate it to the lovely man she last saw a few months ago. Then she goes to see his body at the undertakers. He is like a waxwork. On his breastbone, she can see the end of a stitch where they cut him open and sewed him back up again. He would hate the weird gold embroidered shroud they have dressed him in. His face is a bit red, like he had been in the sun the day he died. She waits for him to jump up and say, 'Fooled you!'

One day his photo will be faded. To her, he is forever young. He lived life at a hundred miles an hour. As if he was running out of time. Despite his fast car, he always arrived late but compensated for it with bottles of wine and presents. Everyone loved him for his quick wit that was rarely unkind. It's not fair. Life is profoundly changed for ever. She cries so much she is thirsty all the time. She will never be happy ever again. His girlfriend is distraught. Her parents and her sister are without the words to express what they feel. At the crematorium, the curtain comes down at the end of the service, and his coffin disappears. They eat sandwiches and drink beer at a pub afterwards because that's what he would have wanted.

I've had a call from my boss asking how I am and when I plan to be back in the office. Both feet are stuck in the mud of grief. Few know what to say to me. They can't know how much my insides scream out for any words of comfort. Looking after the baby forces routine on my disordered mind and broken spirit. Even Grandma's ghost is apparently lost for words. I've sensed her, but not seen her since it happened. Perhaps the awfulness of losing her grandson takes her back to the war years. So much senseless loss of young life. I can guess what she's thinking, 'Ah can't tek it on mah 'ead. It's agin laws o' nature to lose a young'un like 'im. It ain't reight. But lass, yer'll get through this. What dun't kill yer mekes yer stronger.'

Kale (*Brassica oleracea*)

I return to work the Monday after the funeral. 'Are you sure?' my boss asked me kindly on the phone, and then reverted to type, 'It will give you something different to focus on. Better than moping around the house.' When I enter reception, the teary PA gives me a hug. My boss doesn't know what to say, so tells me there's a meeting in half an hour if I feel up to attending it. I worry another bad thing will happen, like the last day I was in the office. Every time the phone goes, I jump. I sit behind my desk and feel the sickness in my stomach. It is always there, reminding me something is not right in my world.

Unlike my brother, I still have a life and I have to try to live it. He wouldn't want me to be beaten. I think of all the notes I received describing how he never gave up when things were tough. To take my mind off things, I start reading some correspondence that has arrived whilst I've been out of the office. The PA comes in, smiles, and says she thinks I might want to take a call that has come in for me. She buzzes it through to my office. I have won a big job that I tendered for a month ago. All my own efforts. It's a sign I have to carry on. I have a husband and a son, and I cannot disappear into my suffering without trace. Over time, I must learn to live with all of this. I pick up my notepad and pen and go and join the meeting. There is work to be done.

CHAPTER 8

Leek (*Allium porrum*)

1986

Dad said Grandma had wanted to die for years. But like a creaking gate, she kept hanging on. As I travel north for Grandma's funeral, I consider the coincidence of her life coming to an end in the same place where I have my earliest memories. Our lives share nothing else in common. Apart of course from 'their Norman', her son and my dad. The book I've brought for the train journey up to Cleethorpes lies unopened on the table next to the medium Americano takeaway coffee from which I'm sipping occasionally. Through the train window, I see the concrete retaining walls and tower blocks of North London being rapidly replaced by endless suburban housing estates and high streets of shops in Hertfordshire.

Although the first female on either side of our family to have gone to university, I'm certainly not the only one with the necessary brains. An accident of fate and timing. My mum went to grammar school, but in her day, only 'blue stockings' did 'A' levels and even fewer went to university. She left Greenhead High School when she was sixteen and enrolled for secretarial college. My dad was a very bright young lad and already a year ahead of his age group at school. His considerably older brother had gone into the RAF after school and persuaded his doubting parents it was the right thing for him to go on to higher education.

It was fully funded of course, but it meant that, during term time, he couldn't earn money to support the family. This was a big deal culturally and economically. But they were persuaded because Dad wanted to be a teacher, so needed a degree. When he went to Nottingham University, he became aware of his strong Yorkshire dialect. Embarrassed because his fellow students couldn't understand him, he enrolled for elocution lessons. Every university vacation he worked in factory jobs so he could give money to his mother for housekeeping.

When he graduated, he took a teaching post in Huddersfield and went into rented lodgings. The story goes that my mum knocked on his landlady's door, selling tickets for the church raffle and that's how they met. So different from my life at a similar age. I live in the 'Big Smoke' as my grandma used to call it, in a maisonette I've just bought with my boyfriend. It's in Finsbury Park, a former red-light district, but 'on the up' according to local estate agent parlance. We live 'over the brush', as my grandparents would say. The subject of getting married occasionally comes up, but neither of us is in a hurry to walk down the aisle. The fact is it won't really change anything. My parents don't really approve of us living together but accept it.

I was fond of my grandma but didn't have a relationship with her independently of my parents. I'm not sure she wanted that, or at least she never sought it out. I was never invited to spend time with her and Grandad without Mum and Dad. Life was a struggle for her, 'she couldn't tek things on in 'er mind'. Her way of saying she had limited physical and emotional capacity. But I feel sad that I didn't see much of my grandma in the last few years. My parents moved away from Lincolnshire to the other side of the country when I left school. When I went back home from university at the end of term, it was miles away from Grandma and Grandad.

I do a job my grandma would never have heard of, still less have had a clue what it entailed. As a recruitment consultant in the City, every morning I put on my corporate uniform and wait with hundreds of others down in the dark tunnel for the train that takes me to the office in Blackfriars. Grandma would have hated everything about it. The crowds, the constant noise of the traffic and the overground trains. Grabbing takeaway coffees and sandwiches, jumping into black taxis, buying ready-made meals or eating out at wine bars would have seemed so frivolous and extravagant to her.

Yet that's what I do, because I can. A bit of me feels uncomfortable about my rather hedonistic lifestyle and the excesses of the City. Grandma and Grandad and all they represent is an important leveller for me. In my head, my current lifestyle isn't for ever. Deep down I know that sooner or later I need to work out what I really want to do. But right now, life is a blast, and I am having fun.

My grandma, Alice Farmer, née Brough may once have been carefree, but I have only ever known her to be weary of life and downtrodden. A former nursing auxiliary, she married Ron, my grandad, when they were both in their early twenties between the two world wars. The story goes that her mother-in-law, known as Nanna, was the catalyst for her perpetually exhausted state.

My dad's family went to live with her after her husband died, which was the reverse of what would normally happen. The reason for this being that, as a miner's widow, she was entitled to unlimited coal as her pension payments for the rest of her life, but only if she stayed in the house she had lived in with my great grandfather before he died. Money was very tight, and the fuel was crucial to sustain the extended family. Every week, the coal would be left on the road outside the terraced house. By all accounts it was a considerable amount and meant they always had a fire in the grate and fuel for cooking. Many families up and down the road had similar arrangements.

Nanna was a large, formidable woman. Some would have called her stout. Large busted, with curlers in her hair and a headscarf over her head, she stomped around making her presence felt. It is said that she made my somewhat fragile grandma pay a big price for living in her house and using her coal allowance by constantly undermining and criticising her. Nothing was quite good enough. The way she kept the house, the food she put on the table, how she raised her two boys, the kind of wife she was. My grandfather worked long shifts as a driver on the railways and left the two women unhappily alone together for long periods.

Motherhood was a further burden for her. Physically small, Mum always described her as 'birdlike'. Her first pregnancy, then confinement, was difficult and left her weak and 'never the same again'. Her first son, my Uncle Ron, was 'plenty' she used to say, so much so that the unplanned arrival of my dad six years later 'finished her off'. Thereafter, she took to 'resting' on her red couch in the spare room every afternoon. She never recovered the tiniest zest for life and was henceforward described by my parents as 'ailing'.

She was a gentle spirit, 'would ne'er 'arm a fly', and I used to feel sorry for her. She never visited her misery on anyone else, never demanded anything from anyone, she was just like a ghost of herself. A woman of few words, any phrases she uttered were full of doom and gloom and, unlike my grandad, she was entirely without humour. Because of this, Grandma Farmer became a figure of fun in our family. 'No one but yer Grandma knows 'ow badly ah feel,' was one of her stock phrases that became much mimicked by us. When we used to visit, we all sat on the edges of our seats waiting for her funny 'grandma expressions', and then stifled our giggles. Even if she realised what we are up to, she was past caring.

They left the terrace council house with the outside loo in Conisborough about five years ago to come and live close to my uncle in Lincolnshire. Uncle Ron was 'something big' in the council and managed to get them a bungalow at the end of the row with an allotment behind it for my grandad to grow his vegetables in. Without this, they wouldn't have countenanced the move. Grandad spent most of his waking hours in his allotment. It was a thing of beauty, alright. Neat, perfectly spaced rows of thriving green crops. He always used to say that you must start with beans at the back as they grow the tallest. Then he told me he planted the other crops in front of them in strict alphabetical order, so he could remember what everything was. I'm not sure now if he was pulling my leg or not. I wouldn't put it past him as he always had a twinkle in his eye.

The smell of cooking greeted us when we went into the kitchen through the back door. A big pot on the electric hob would be bubbling away. Grandad had nearly always 'fetched something in' that he had dug up from the allotment and it would be waiting in the sink for Grandma's attention. When it was leeks, my dad always used to marvel, 'Just look at the size of those. I wish I could grow leeks like that. It's the home-made compost he uses.' I politely nodded.

As a child I never liked the taste of leeks. Ever since my school days when the dinner ladies cut them lengthways into ribbons, then they were boiled within an inch of their lives and covered in tasteless thick white sauce. They were served in giant metallic containers. Generally cold by the time they had been wheeled across the playground on a trolley from the kitchen, I hated their slimy texture so was inclined to eat them without chewing, frequently choking as a result. Not eating them or making a big fuss over the matter brought public shaming and disapproval from my teacher, so I learnt to have a huge gulp of water after each disgusting mouthful, thereby managing to leave a clean plate. Grandma used to say they were best served in soups and stews.

Grandma never ate with us when we visited. Dad said it was a habit she formed during the war. She took just enough to survive on, so the men in the family had more. 'Yer get plenty,' she used to say to us all, 'ah've already 'ad mine.' But Dad said she always ate afterwards, and only if there was any left after we had finished. I used to worry that if I had seconds, she would go hungry. So, I always said I was full up and couldn't eat any more. I used to go back into the kitchen after everyone had moved through to the sitting room, pretending I was going to see Grandad in the garden. But really, I wanted to check there were some leftovers for Grandma and that she wasn't going to get any thinner.

She often talked about the war and the coupons that were necessary to buy food. She bought as little as possible, preferring to make meals from what Grandad was able to grow in his allotment, bulking the vegetables out with pearl barley. He kept seeds back at the end of the growing season to plant the next year. Even after the war was over and rationing finished, Grandma continued to keep the house in a frugal way. Nothing was wasted. My dad and uncle 'tipped up' money from any wages they earnt to my grandma. My grandfather handed his pay packet to her and she managed every penny, only giving my grandfather beer money at the end of the week if there was sufficient left. There were no luxuries. My dad was given an orange at Christmas as a huge treat.

She spent all day inside the bungalow whilst Grandad worked in his garden or went for his daily walk along the seafront. She would tidy round in the mornings, and then, after dinner, which was always at midday, she would rest. The red couch had moved with them from Conisborough and was now in the tiny spare bedroom at the front of the bungalow. Because their bungalow was on the end, few people passed by which meant she got the peace and quiet she yearned. She was a very shy woman, and if she had to go out to the shops, she avoided anyone who might want to pass the time of day. 'There's note so queer as folk,' she used to say, 'ah prefer to keep mysen to mysen, better that way.'

There was always a small pile of hardback library books on the sitting room table and Grandad went every week to exchange them. They shared a pair of reading glasses and took turns to read. To make conversation, Dad once asked what she was reading, 'Ah, they're just a bit o' stuff an' nonsense but it passes a bit of time reight enough.' I used to wonder if she sometimes secretly imagined she was a character in one of her escapist novels.

When she and Grandad came to stay at our house every Christmas, she used to put her ill-fitting false teeth in for the occasion. She 'didn't want to be a bother' for the dentist, so instead put up with them clattering around her mouth when she spoke or ate.

When she was at home, she 'made herself tidy' after her afternoon rest. She put a grip in her straight short hair on one side of the parting and placed a beige chiffon scarf secured with a brooch around her thin neck to keep the draughts off. The slightest blast of cold air resulted in another ache or pain to be added to the already significant list. One day she asked me to go and fetch her cardigan from the bedroom, as she felt cold after lying down. The room was full of dark furniture with an overwhelming smell of carbolic soap. Her cardigan was in a lavender scented bag in the wardrobe and I found it just where she said it would be. There was absolutely nothing decorative or pretty in there, except a beautiful silver comb, hairbrush and mirror on the dressing table.

A port and lemon lasted Grandma for the whole of Christmas Day. She only had it to keep everyone happy and resisted any attempt to have it freshened up, saying she had 'plenty'. She chided my grandad who was intent on enjoying himself, 'Gi' o'er Ron. Yer'll get as daft as a brush if yer sup anymore.' She ate her dinner silently and without expression. When she could eat no more, she used to say to Mum, 'Ah've enjoyed every mouthful, but ah don't think ah can manage another thing till tomorro'. Thanks pet.' Grandad, meanwhile, ate like he may never see another meal again. 'Aah, that scran were reight grand,' he would say, smacking his lips loudly and helping himself to seconds, 'Don't mind if ah do,' he grinned. 'I'd rather feed you for a week than a month,' Mum used to laugh.

I suddenly realise we're pulling into Sheffield and I need to change trains. I find the platform I need for my connection. There's a cold wind blowing. The smaller local train is noisier but has few other passengers in my carriage. I pick up my book and read a few chapters as we head towards the east coast. Neither the book nor the scenery is gripping, so I doze for half an hour, waking up as we come into Cleethorpes Station. I imagine I might feel a connection with this place where I was born and lived the first seven years of my life, but however hard I try to tune into something profound, there is nothing. I walk past the station buffet, which is closed, towards the uniformed ticket collector who does his job wordlessly.

Mum and Dad are waiting for me outside in the car, having driven over from Cheshire. We exchange pleasantries about our respective journeys, and how nice it is to see each other, albeit in sad circumstances. Dad is matter of fact about the occasion at hand. 'Well we've got plenty of time. And it looks like the rain may hold off,' he says, peering out of the windscreen. 'I don't know what to expect,' I say, 'I haven't been to a funeral before.' Dad looks at me through the driver's mirror, 'Well there's nothing much to it. The coffin is brought into the church. We sing a few hymns, the minister says a few words and then we go out into the churchyard for the burial.' I hadn't expected this. 'Burial?' I ask. 'Yes, your grandma didn't want to be cremated. Grandad has bought a double plot, one for her and one for him.'

We arrive outside the church and park the car. There are a handful of people outside, all family. Grandad has his Sunday best suit on and his black tie. He has shrunk as he has got older, so everything looks too big on him. He straightens his trilby hat and takes his white handkerchief out to wipe his watery eyes. I give him a hug, but I don't know what to say, and am distracted by the hearse bearing her coffin, which is approaching. The undertakers are a well-ordered team. It feels disrespectful to look too intently at the wooden coffin carrying Grandma as it is carefully unloaded on to a trolley. This finale in a box, which awaits all of us, seems such an anti-climax after all the ups and downs of a long life. And yet this is what Grandma had been longing for. An uninterrupted rest.

Grandma is wheeled into church with Grandad then the rest of us following her. I go into the pew first, followed by Mum and Dad who sit next to the aisle. The minister stands behind the coffin at the front. He offers a warm welcome and invites us to follow the order of service. Dad looks sad and thoughtful. I look around at everyone. Some look at the floor, others stare into the middle distance. I look at her coffin, but I feel no connection with it. I feel my eyes travelling upwards to the ceiling and I imagine Grandma lying on her red couch in the sky. Finally, she doesn't have to be bothered by anyone. I wonder if she will get bored of resting all day, every day.

I return my gaze to the photo of Grandma on the front of the order of service. It was taken one Christmas at the house we used to live in. I recognise the dining room French windows behind the table which has crackers and holly on it. She is sitting alongside Grandad. He is grinning broadly, and she is unsmiling but looking directly at the camera. That's just how I remember her. I look up and glance sideways at Dad, who hasn't changed his expression. Then something makes me glance the other way.

Her ghost is not dissimilar to how she looked when she was alive, except her hair is softer, less straight and she is wearing pink and grey, not beige. Her face wears an unfamiliar animated expression. She looks steely. She crosses her legs, leans forward and looks at me intently, 'Pet, now ah want yer to think on. Yer a good lass. Meke yer parents proud. And yer doin' well fer thissen down in the smoke. But thou musn't lose sight of what thou wants in life. Be true to thissen and yer'll be reight. And another thing. It's high time yer stopped living o'er brush wi' that young fella o' yers. 'Ee needs to mek an honest woman out o' thee. Reight, ah've said mah piece and ah'll keep mah counsel now. Ah'll be seein' thee.'

After she disappears, her message hovers in the air as we sing the final hymn. Now she's asked the question, I'm at a loss for the answer. What do I want in life? I'm just following my nose, making life up as it happens. Is that such a bad thing? I wish I did have a great passion in life, like being a doctor or an artist. But I don't, or at least if I do, I am not yet aware of it. And how would I go about finding it anyway?

Leek (*Allium porrum*)

The hymn finished, we are invited to join the minister at the graveside in the churchyard, where we will bury 'Alice's mortal remains and lay her to rest'. But it's not her mortal remains that I'm thinking about as we stand around the freshly dug hole in the ground. I like the new ballsy grandma. Perhaps that's how she used to be before Nanna and motherhood came along. Grandad throws some earth onto the top of the coffin. 'Ah'll be seein' thee Grandma,' I say to myself as I peer down into the darkness at the wooden lid with a cross and a handful of soil on it.

On the train back to London, I put my book down and think some more about Grandma's words. Maybe, one day, there'll be a bolt of lightning and my life purpose will be revealed. In the meantime, I'll muddle along. And as for getting married, well maybe that's not such a bad idea. After all, what are we waiting for?

CHAPTER 9

Lettuce (*Lactuca sativa*)

1972–2020

1997

It's a Sunday afternoon and it's been raining ever since we got up around 6am. It was still dark when we had breakfast. We have watched the *Jungle Book* video twice, played about ten games of snap, built a Lego castle and done umpteen jigsaws. We keep thinking the weather is going to clear for long enough to go to the park, but at 4pm it's still pouring down and we need to get out of the house. I make a plan and purposefully get everyone's shoes and coats on, check the nappy bag is fully loaded with a spare of everything, strap the baby in the pushchair and make a quick dash for the loo before we set out.

I started off with all sorts of lofty ideals with regards to feeding my children. It's going to be 'homemade everything', just like I had been brought up with. No picky eaters. My children will try everything, including mushrooms, olives and aubergines. It's simply a matter of introducing things at an early age, so they get used to the different flavours. I would shop for fresh produce at the local market. I would cook ahead and freeze all sorts of nutritious family meals that I would then produce effortlessly. Everything would run like clockwork.

I see my reflection in the mirror of the downstairs toilet and realise that I haven't yet combed my hair today. I can hear World War Three breaking out in the hall, so I hurry back to see what is going on. They want to take their toy swords, and their dad has just confiscated them. I grab my woolly hat and pull it over my slept-on hair.

'Right, everyone, let's go.'

Lettuce (*Lactuca sativa*)

As I bump the pushchair down the front steps, I hear grumblings and the door being locked behind me,

'I can't believe we are going to actually do this. McDonalds for goodness sake!'

'McDonalds. Yeah.' The boys look up at us. They are bursting with anticipation but also confused, as they have been indoctrinated that fast food is the devil incarnate.

'What have we come to?' their dad asks disapprovingly. But he too is too tired to argue.

2006

I go into battle over lettuce. My dad always grew loads of it, and once I got over finding the occasional snail that continued to cling stubbornly to a leaf despite being washed, it became like any other vegetable I was presented with, and I ate it gratefully. The mother of my French exchange partner used to serve lettuce every day in between the meat dish and the cheese course, along with a creamy vinaigrette dressing that I came to love, especially dipping my baguette in the oily residue left on my plate.

Ever since the children have been small, I often put a bowl of salad out to be eaten with the main courses at dinner time. Which they never touch. I'm becoming anxious the only thing they will eat is peas, and on very good days, broccoli. So, I decide on a new strategy. I make homemade burgers, get some bread buns from the baker and put out sliced tomatoes, lettuce and mayonnaise. They look contemptuously at the green stuff.

'Really Mum, the lettuce isn't necessary and doesn't add anything.'

'McDonalds put lettuce in their burgers.' I had anticipated the objection and am quick off the mark, 'The crunch of the lettuce is good with burgers. Try it.'

'Mum lettuce is just... There's no point to it. Why are you making us eat it?' Unhappy faces all round and then they get a whiff of something else, 'Have you sneaked mushrooms into the burgers?'

'No,' I say, not definitively enough.

'Yes, you have. We can taste it. You know we don't eat mushrooms. Why do you have to do this? And why do we have to have homemade burgers anyway? They taste weird. And they've got loads of onions in them.'

'Look you lot. Sometime between now and your eighteenth birthdays, you will all come to like both lettuce and mushrooms. So, think about it, it might as well be today.'

'No, it won't be.'

'Oh, for goodness sake. Just put lots of tomato ketchup on it. It will drown out the things you don't like.'

'McDonalds burgers are better. Why can't we have them like everyone else does?'

2004

My goal to cook from scratch every day using fresh locally sourced ingredients is ancient history. It's a game of day-to-day survival. But I still can't let go of appearing to be the perfect provider. Pots of ready-made fresh pasta sauce and frozen pizzas get hidden guiltily at the bottom of the supermarket trolley, with all the healthy fresh stuff piled on top.

The constant honing of my juggling skills never seems to keep up with growing appetites, more calendar entries and the increased demands of work. I actually begin to run between tasks, believing it will save the odd vital second or two. My weekly swim has become my monthly swim, but at least ticks the 'trying to keep fit' box. When I very occasionally make it to a Pilates class, I reflect that I would pay the teacher the full amount just to be allowed to lie on my mat on the heated floor for an hour.

My only true respite is going to the hairdressers once every six weeks, when I sit comatose in the chair, not being bothered by anyone other than to be asked whether I want a cup of coffee. I don't even care what I will look like when I leave the salon. I've started having my colour done as well as the cut and blow dry, mainly because I was shamed into it by my hairdresser who told me what a dreadful hash I was making of it at home. But also because it adds at least an hour onto each appointment and I can devour several back copies of *Hello* magazine, albeit I look like an alien from outer space as I sit cocooned in a white plastic gown with my hair wrapped in tin foil. After the pampering is complete and the stylist says, 'There you go, all done now,' I feel like weeping and often ask, 'Can I please stay?'

The last thing I need is a letter in a schoolbag announcing a dreaded cake sale. Not only do I literally not have any spare time to make something, but it also pushes all the 'I'm an inadequate mother' buttons. Other mothers arrive at the school gates on the appointed day with a creation that Mary Berry would be proud of. 'Oh, we had such a lovely afternoon, the children and me. Baking is one of our favourite things. Everybody took turns to decorate. It was such fun.'

Whilst in our Lake District house last half term, I thought how nice it would be to do some baking. The boys expressed only mild enthusiasm, but I decided to strike whilst the iron was hot. I asked what they wanted to make. 'Doughnuts,' they cried. 'I was thinking of something a bit 'cakier',' I said. Eventually we landed on muffins. They helped me do the weighing out. I turned my back to get the bun tins and mixing bowl out of the cupboard. In that moment, I heard one of them shout, 'Come on, let's go outside. Call us when it's time to lick out the bowl Mum.' And the next thing I hear is the back door being slammed shut, followed by a football being thumped against the garden wall.

For the cake sale, I go to Sainsburys and buy some posh mince pies, so they are more likely to pass for homemade ones. I get them home and rough them up with the back of a spoon, then dredge them with icing sugar. I think they look good, but not suspiciously perfect. When I collect the boys later that day, the teacher gives me back the still almost full plate with an apologetic 'you've done your best but need to try harder' look on her face.

1972

I can see the big smoke-stained chimneys to the left out of the car window. 'Are we nearly there?' my brother asks. 'Another half hour,' Mum says. We go up the steep hill at the back of Fartown Rugby Club and turn left into the driveway. Mum's mum, my grandma, gets out of her chair when she hears us coming up the steps. She walks a bit more stiffly since the last time we visited. Mum says she needs a new hip. I wonder what will happen to the old one. We go through to the living room, where the electric fire is on and the usual tray with potted meat sandwiches and fruit cake is laid out. Eating on our knees is such a treat. We polish everything off whilst Mum and Dad have cups of tea and chat above our heads.

On Saturday teatime I'm first out of the car and up the steps to the neat terrace belonging to Mum's aunt and uncle, Great Aunt Lizzie and Great Uncle Stanley. It's the other side of Huddersfield near the park we sometimes go to. 'Well how lovely to see you all,' they clap their hands with joy and surprise when they see us. There are net curtains in the window and a grandmother clock with a rhythmic tick tock in the hall. Auntie Lizzie has a kind face and a round body. She wears patterned, loosely fitting dresses, sensible lace up shoes and an apron tied around her waist. They don't have children, only nieces and nephews. When I ask Mum why, I'm told it's not the done thing to ask a question like that.

Their front parlour is taken up with Uncle Stanley's chiropody surgery so we all crowd into the back room. We children sit on upright chairs whilst my mum and dad sit in the comfortable chairs. Auntie Lizzie fetches a kitchen stool for herself.

'Well, you'll never guess what we're having for tea,' she says.

'Fish and chips!' we shout.

'How did you guess?' she laughs.

We always have the same. We hear the bubbling oil, then the sound of the fish going into the pan. Finally, the shaking of the wire basket as the chips are cooked. It is served with a big plate of white bread and butter and a pot of tea. After tea,

Uncle Stanley does magic tricks with a sixpence. His white collars are stiff and look rather uncomfortable. He pulls up his shirt sleeves with a silver elasticated garter. If I am lucky, I am allowed to sit in the big chair in his chiropody treatment room, which he lowers and raises using the foot pedal. I wonder whether what he does to his patients is painful.

On Sunday, before we head home again, Grandma cooks Yorkshire pudding and roast beef, followed by bilberry pie and custard. I do my homework on the little kitchen table whilst she sings and gets the meal ready. Sunday lunch is always served on the big square table in the dining room overlooking the neat lawn with the little statue of a dog in the corner. To start we have pieces of a giant Yorkshire pudding with gravy. The crockery has square shaped borders with small orange and red flowers. Grandad always carves the meat whilst Grandma bustles around. Dad says the man of the household must always carve. When the bilberry pie and custard is served, the pre-departure talk starts. Possible weekends when they might visit us next and key events that will take place before then. As we leave, we are given a sweet for the car journey home.

2020

It's Christmas morning at the end of a bizarre year. About 20 years ago, I started a tradition of going to family service, so that everyone was reminded of the true meaning of Christmas. Covid has put paid to any 'in person' church services, so instead we decide to take breakfast and eat it on top of a mountain. Feels kind of spiritual and picnics are part of our family folklore.

When the children were small, they protested loudly at the

idea of 'going for a walk'. So, this activity was rechristened 'going on an expedition', which sounded so much more compelling, especially if there was food involved. Of course, there were always significant negotiations about the point at which we should eat the picnic. 'We have to get to the top first,' says one. 'It's blowing a gale, let's stop here because it is sheltered, and it's well past lunchtime,' says another. Sandwich content is strictly controlled. 'Mum, why have you made me the worst sandwiches in the history of the world? I hope you can imagine me sitting hungry and miserable at the back of the bus.' (Text message from son whilst on a school trip.)

Cheese must be grated. Cheddar is acceptable, but not any kind of blue cheese or creamy cheese with a rind. Chutney is a 'no no', as is too much 'unnecessary salad stuff'. When I first started to make soup, that we transported in a flask, there were howls of indignation, 'We prefer Heinz tomato soup. Why do we have to have Mum's random green stuff?'

This Christmas Day morning, everything is being laid out on the kitchen table ready to be packed in rucksacks. We will walk for about an hour before reaching the top of Eyecott Hill, which boasts a great view of Blencathra. Naturally, everyone has a view on what we should take and how it is to be cooked and eaten.

'Dad, we can't cook scrambled eggs for six people in that ridiculous little camping pot. We need a wider pan than that, otherwise they'll never get done. And it's freezing out there. We don't want to be hanging around.'

'It's ideal, specially designed for camping. We'll take two pots. One for the eggs and one for the bacon.'

'That's ridiculous. You can't get the bacon to crisp in that thing. And what about the beans? What are we going to heat them up in?'

'We can heat them up in the same pan after the scrambled eggs are done.'

'But the whole point is to eat everything together.'

'Don't make a fuss. It will be fine. Oh, and we need to take the special smoked salmon as well. It's Christmas after all.'

'The place at the top where we're having the picnic is narrow and rocky. And it's uneven. Aren't we making this all a bit complicated?'

'Stop intefering. We need to leave room in one backpack for the champagne and fresh orange juice. We always have that on Christmas Day at breakfast time.'

'Can't we have it when we get back. Have a glass whilst we're opening presents. Let's just take coffee and make it easier?'

'No. We've got to have champagne.'

'How are we going serve all of this food? What are we going to eat it on?'

'On the bread baps. Just pile everything on them.'

'What, everything at once? And the beans as a second course?'

'Dad this is ridiculous, I'm going to pack another bigger saucepan. And some plates, knives and forks. Have you got the mayonnaise and the tomato ketchup?'

'Don't be daft. If we take all that lot, we can't take the champagne.'

'It's not meant to be a three-course meal complete with

wine tasting, just an alternative to going to church. It was supposed to be fun. And by the way, it's just started to rain.'

2005

I decide to buy a bread maker. Despite all my efforts, the boys like the white sliced loaves the best. One of the mothers at school is always going on about the irresistible smell of home-baked brown loaves and how her children can't get enough of the stuff. As soon as I have bought it and got it in the house, without even taking my coat off, I unpack it and read the instructions. No time like the present. I grab my purse and car keys and shout to the boys downstairs, 'Just popping to Sainsbury's.' Half an hour later I'm back and start measuring out the ingredients and put them all into the loaf tin. I set the timer before I go upstairs to bed so it will be ready for breakfast. Next morning, I run down ahead of everyone else so I can take it out of the machine and put it like a trophy in the middle of the breakfast table. It smells amazing.

'What is that?' I am greeted by.

'A homemade loaf of bread, it will be delicious.'

Much wrinkling of noses. 'But it's brown.'

'Brown bread is much better for you than white. And homemade tastes completely different from the ones you buy in shops.'

'It looks weird. We prefer sliced bread.'

'Well, I can slice it if that's what you want.'

'We like Hovis ready sliced white bread. When you slice it at home, it's not the same. Can't you get some next time you go to the supermarket?'

They are persuaded to try a tiny bit of it,

'It's a bit solid. Like a brick. Mum why can't we have what we always have?'

Hungry, they go and find the Coco Pops cereal box in the cupboard. Another failure of motherhood. I was always adamant they could only have Cornflakes or Weetabix.

2007

Upstairs, I can hear stomping around, cupboards being rummaged through and doors being slammed. Then boys arguing. After a while, they realise they're going to be late for school if they don't get a move on. One by one, they run downstairs. I hear their footsteps slightly dampened by the carpet on the stairs, then amplified by the wooden floorboards in the hall. The last 'Bye Mum' is cut in two by the slam of the door behind them. Their dad left hours ago to catch a train to London.

He just wants me to be happy. I try to eat some breakfast, but I can't get the toast to go down. I don't understand what's happening with me. I have a situation most people would give their eye teeth for. A lovely family, beautiful home and finally, a fulfilling job. I've been feeling like this for a few months now. I don't recognise myself, bursting into tears all the time and feeling so lethargic and tired.

Having once yearned a bit of peace and quiet, after the children leave for school, I find the silence of the house uncomfortable and oppressive. I sit staring into space and avoid seeing my friends because I feel I have nothing positive to say. I recognise the 'darkness' I have read about in the problem pages of women's magazines.

Everyone around me seems self-absorbed and purposeful,

but I am lost. Every day, I sit here at the table and think about how the day stretches out in front of me. It seems to have no meaning. I make myself clear up what remains of the breakfast detritus on the kitchen table and pour the last dregs from the cafetière into my 'Best Mum in the World' mug. I flick through this month's copy of *Good Housekeeping*, but I have no energy for cooking. I make things that require minimal effort but will fill everyone up. Just pushing the supermarket trolley round is hard work, and when I get home I've forgotten half the things I need. Everything gets eaten in five minutes flat anyway, so what difference does it make?

A letter on the health page takes my eye. A woman writes in who could be me. Same age. Same symptoms. Same story. The doctor replies that she suspects she may be menopausal and recommends speaking to her GP about HRT. I received no post-operative advice after having a hysterectomy just over a year ago, save to take it easy for six weeks. I immediately feel lighter. Maybe I'm not going mad and make an appointment to see my GP. It feels so unfair that women have to contend with this too, after all the years of periods and childbearing. She is supportive and patient, explains what happens when women go 'through the change' and says the good news is that I don't have to put up with feeling as I do. So, I try a course of magic HRT pills, and life returns to how it was.

2008

I hear the chatter as they come into the front drive. The front door with the plain glass window opens with a great whoosh. A troop of boys lands in the hallway, bags dumped just far enough inside to be able to close the door. The stained glass was shattered shortly after moving in by a football. 'It wasn't my fault. He was rugby tackling me and made me throw it at a weird angle.'

The troop hurries down the four steep steps into the kitchen. 'Starving' is all that they have energy to get out. They look at me pleadingly. I point to the bowl of batter on the table, ready to make pancakes on the AGA. 'Yes!' they chorus and sit down expectantly. They scan the things I've put out to make sure nothing is missing. Sugar and lemon juice, jam, butter. One of them notices there is no Nutella out and goes to get it. I sigh, 'Don't smother that horrible stuff all over them.' I am ignored.

I do the first batch. I flip them over after a couple of minutes and they brown on the other side. I hurry them to the table, where the feeding frenzy begins. There is grabbing of preferred toppings and then they are eaten before I can finish spooning the next dollops of batter onto the greased silicone. I cook batch after batch until the mixing bowl is empty. They lean back in their chairs, rub their stomachs like satiated young cubs. Then, if I am lucky, they might even start to tell me about their days. After answering a couple of questions, eventually one of them says, 'PlayStation anyone?' and down they go to the TV room in the basement to hang out with the dog.

2013

The holidays are the worst. I come down every morning at 7:00am. I know what will be waiting for me. I clear up the 'snack' they had before they went to bed. I do not have to be a detective to guess what they had. Open cupboards, half empty packets and tins, dirty plates and cutlery provide all the clues

I need. Frying pans caked in solidified fat, but with tell-tale traces of baked beans, eggs, or bacon. The tomato sauce bottle is still on the table. The house is silent with sleeping boys. Shoes and discarded items of clothing all over the stairs and hallway give me a clue to how many extras we might have.

I go down to the cellar to unload the washing machine. The TV room door is shut, which probably means there are a couple of bodies in there too. I use the term loosely. I attend meetings or work in my office like a normal person keeping normal hours. Around 12 noon or later they will appear for breakfast. More frying pans, more bacon, more tomato ketchup. About 4pm it's their lunchtime and they manage to peel themselves off the sofa to feed again. Usually pasta. On a good day, the dirty plates get moved to the top of the dishwasher, their attempt at clearing up, in response to me 'going on'.

When I finally catch up with them, I tell them Grandma and Grandad are coming for dinner on Friday evening and please can they not be so hungover or tired they can only grunt. And please can everyone not just have eaten and be clean and preferably tidy. And if they want to go out afterwards, after an appropriate length of time, they can.

'What's for scran when Grandma and Grandad come?' they chorus.

'Steak and kidney pie.'

'Brave move. Grandma's pie is the best. And she makes her own shortcrust pastry.'

'Yes, I'm fully aware of that, but I don't. Life is too short. I get it from Sainsbury's.'

Mum says she will bring a pudding because she knows how

busy I am. And I'm not very good at puddings unless it's a crumble so this is good news. My parents arrive with half the house as usual. An overnight bag. Two bottles of wine, some homemade tiffin in an empty margarine carton for the boys, a freezer box with the pudding in it and some chocolates.

'Don't worry, we haven't come for three weeks,' Dad quips. 'Hello boys. Lovely to see you all. So, how are we?'

'Good,' they all say.

'Do you want a sherry Mum?'

'Oh, thought you'd never ask. Wouldn't say no.'

'What's in the freezer box Mum?'

'Oh yes. Well, I said I would bring pudding. Didn't think you'd mind but I bought a couple of those arctic rolls and a readymade lemon meringue pie from Morrison's. The arctic rolls need to go in the freezer.'

'Readymade? But you make everything from scratch.'

'Well, I don't anymore. What's the point when you can buy it in the shops?'

2019

It's Sunday morning and we walk through the well-heeled streets of Pimlico, Central London. The restaurants and bars are being swept to ready them for lunchtime service. There are vintage clothes and record shops, specialist food shops and estate agents' windows to peer into as we saunter along. We are visiting for the weekend. The two eldest boys have both lived in London since university and have suggested we all have brunch.

'Mum, can you get a move on, we're starving.'

The conversation of the previous evening had covered the

merits and demerits of being a vegetarian or whether it is ok to eat locally produced meat or responsibly sourced fish. The youth claimed to be on the moral high ground, with their disapproval of taking multiple flights a year, food air miles and almond milk. Somehow the conversation always turned back on our own inadequacies.

We find a seat in the basement of this trendy café. The menu is a clipboard full of well-turned pages. We order flat whites all round.

'Where are the newspapers?' I ask.

'What?' The boys look at me as if I am a Luddite.

'When we were young, we used to sit in places like this and read the Sunday papers for hours. It's the only thing for a hangover.'

'Mum, people don't read newspapers these days.' One gets his phone out of his pocket. 'What do you think these are for?'

The waitress arrives, 'Do you all know what you would like?'

'A fresh mango juice, smashed avocado, smoked salmon, and poached eggs on toasted sourdough,' says one.

'Same for me please but with crispy bacon instead of smoked salmon.'

Unable to resist the opportunity, their dad sighs dramatically and quips, 'Not very good for your eco credentials, lads. Just think about all those carbon emissions.'

But they always have the last 'environmentally woke' word. As a team they sense their opportunity. One says, 'Oh yes, Dad. Sorry we forgot. You're obviously the expert on all of this.' The other then moves in to deliver the killer blow, 'Yes Dad. That's rich coming from someone who once said that humans aren't meant to be vegetarian because lions eat giraffes.'

CHAPTER 10

Mangetout
(*Pisum sativum var. saccharatum*)

2000–2001

June 2000 and little do I realise it, but the so-called Tuscany plan is being hatched, right over there. We are by the swimming pool and the sky is so blue, it doesn't look real. I mistakenly think he is engrossed in his book, sitting in one of the white plastic outdoor chairs underneath the parasol. His way of switching off. The children are playing games in the pool, which are getting ever more boisterous. I look up from my novel as it's a matter of time before there are tears or arguments. But they could be drowning in front of him and he wouldn't notice. I envy that ability to focus, to cut out the background noise however loud it becomes and carry on concentrating on the matter in front of you.

But in truth it is double edged, as most things in life are. Many times, senior leaders will reflect in future coaching sessions with me, 'What's it all been about? I haven't been present at some important moments in my life with the people I love best.' And certainly, few people on their death beds wish they had spent more time at work.

In parallel, I am convinced that my inability to focus, no matter what the distractions, started early in my first maternity leave, when some primaeval instinct responded to the desperate cry of a hungry baby. Being able to give attention to two things simultaneously is something I have had to learn to do. I have become adept at switching backwards and forwards between activities requiring different parts of my brain. A gift and a curse. It allowed me more access to the children as they were growing up but could also be frustrating. What I would sometimes have given for the luxury of being able to concentrate completely on the matter in hand.

Mangetout (*Pisum sativum var. saccharatum*)

School holidays epitomised this. I would generally designate a few days to keep free, but on others had to work from my home office whilst trying to ensure that not too much time was being spent on the PlayStation. Inevitably client issues would arise that needed to be dealt with and one day I asked the boys' dad to work from home as I had to go to a meeting in town and couldn't look after them. I returned around 2pm, and as soon as I put the key in the door, I heard the bedlam going on inside. He was working at his desk amidst children fighting and shouting for his attention to intervene. I went into his office and shrugged my shoulders at him, as if to say, 'Hello. Can I not leave the house for a couple of hours without returning to World War Three? What is going on here?' He scarcely looked up from his laptop to tell me he hadn't heard the commotion around him. 'Did you make lunch for them?' I inquired, but I knew the answer. Still with my coat on, I head towards the kitchen, 'Mum we're starving. Dad didn't even make us any lunch.'

As the Tuscan sun is going down, we eat dinner and afterwards the boys go outside to play. I ask what has been absorbing him, and he shares with me his ambition to start a consultancy business. I gulp. 'How big?' I ask. 'Probably 30 or 40 people. It's got to be that big, so we can do some worthwhile projects.' He's thought it all through. I must continue my job as a head-hunter for a few years, 'so we can still eat'. Then, when the business is established, I should stop and do 'something I really want to do'. I've been talking about trying to re-invent myself for some time now, but at the back of my mind I have known something like this might be on the cards and that my head-hunting salary would be an essential component in mitigating the risk.

A determined man, I knew the dye was cast and his mind was made up. To start with, he skips around, energised by the freedom and his escape from corporate shackles. He commissions a graphic designer and chooses artwork for the new logo. He wins his first contract. He recruits his first employee. The business is successful and grows. With ever more mouths to feed, suddenly it's not a lifestyle business anymore. The informal coffee meetings where a few people gather, discuss and agree turn into board meetings, all day affairs with directors, agendas, cash flow projections and project management tools. I know all the worries, concerns, and secrets.

He takes his responsibilities seriously. And now there are many families who rely on the company continuing to be successful. He wants to do things the right way, because he is a good man with strong values and principles. His resilience is remarkable but sometimes he is so tired that by the time he gets home, he can barely speak.

The boys love his stories and wait in their beds, hoping to hear the front door open announcing Daddy is back. However weary, he runs upstairs shouting, 'I'm home, who wants a story?' but then his eyes inevitably close as he lies next to one of them, the open book by his side. A face appears over the bannister, 'Mummy, Daddy's fallen asleep again and he hasn't even finished the story.' He comes downstairs for dinner having washed his face to try and wake himself up. I am incredibly proud of what he has achieved, but at times I resent how it takes him away from us.

Our salvation is the time we spend in our holiday home in Cumbria. The lack of Wi-Fi or mobile phone signal is liberating. The Renault Espace loaded with food, three bathed children in their pyjamas and two cats takes us up the M6 on a Friday evening to rediscover family life. We play cards in front of the big log burner, we go for walks and bike rides. We eat pie and chips at the pub. Endless games of football in the garden. Afternoons spent damming the river, building treehouses, making huge fires. After dark, the boys run round the garden with torches playing hide and seek. The magic ends on Sunday afternoon. In the summer, we have a BBQ on the sunny terrace and then reluctantly pack the car with boys and cats to travel back. Until Preston, we listen and sing along to the Top 40, but once we see the signs to Manchester, the weight of the forthcoming week makes its presence felt.

It's Tuesday September 11th, 2001. As I walk towards the BA Executive Lounge, I hear the robotic announcement, 'The 6.30am British Airways flight to London Heathrow is delayed. Further information to follow.'

I want to cry. It is 6.15am, and I have been up since 4.45am. It's not fully light. From the executive lounge, I can see the engineers' van with its flashing orange light moving slowly across the airfield towards the plane. I have little patience with the situation. It happens regularly. No matter how tiny the issue, it means an hour added onto the scheduled departure time. My already busy day has started off badly. Far too early to call the office to warn the PA my carefully arranged schedule may need to be rejigged. Thank goodness my client meeting is this afternoon.

I know the shuttle timetable between London and Manchester off by heart. It will be another two years before Virgin high speed trains come along and provide a faster alternative to flying. The head-hunting firm where I work is ridiculously London-centric. All internal meetings take place there, and most candidates and clients prefer it. Meetings on conference call are discouraged. 'You need to get the cut of someone's gib,' the managing partner says, 'look them in the eye.'

The minimum time I need between setting my alarm and checking in for my flight is about one hour. At 5.00am I shower and put on my work clothes, which were lain out the night before. My overnight bag is ready and waiting by the front door. I have one that perfectly fits in the overhead cabin locker. My sponge bag is permanently packed with all the essentials, including paracetamol and Lemsips, because I always seem to have a cold, or a headache.

I quickly put a bit of makeup on, though when I snooze on the plane, it all gets smudged. I drive the five miles to the airport and park on the third floor of the multi-storey car park opposite the Departures sliding entrance doors. Once through check-in and screening, I go into the business lounge and grab a coffee. I survey everyone else in the business lounge. They all look pale and knackered. Mirror versions of myself, except most of them are men.

They have all helped themselves to a complimentary newspaper. They turn over the pages impatiently, to get to the business section as quickly as possible. Then they flatten the pages loudly and start to read. The men always sit with their legs wide open, taking up as much space as possible. The few women there are sit with their legs neatly crossed and gently scan the pages for items of interest. Some are fast asleep and snore. We all belong to the club of sleep deprived, regular commuters.

'The delayed 6.30am flight to Heathrow is ready for immediate boarding through gate B.' Only forty-five minutes late. A blast of damp air blows into the business lounge from the airfield. We all know what to do. Wordlessly we queue, say good morning to the stewardess who always does this shift, and then climb the steps to the plane. With a bit of luck, we'll make up a bit of time on the way. At least the recently opened Heathrow Express train direct into Paddington has cut out a bit of travel time the other end. I get on the plane and am dozing restlessly when I hear the engines power up for take-off.

Life at the top of the greasy pole is not all it's made out to be. I didn't set out to become a partner. 'The cream always rises to the top,' my boss says. There are perks. I have lunches and dinners in expensive restaurants that I wouldn't otherwise eat in. I stay in luxury hotels and travel business class. I go to conferences in exotic places like Bermuda and Arizona. I have a wardrobe of sharp pleated skirts and tailored jackets. I don't have to shop in sales anymore. Life at home is comfortable. Nice holidays. A nanny to help with the children.

But there is a constant niggle in my head. Yes, I have been successful, but is this all really me? Sometimes it feels like a parallel universe to the one most people inhabit. I don't always feel comfortable inhabiting a world where everyone is privileged and well off. My husband's firm is going well. I think increasingly about stopping all of this. I have no space to think about what I would really like to do.

I read of the recruitment successes I have been involved with in the *Financial Times*. I am on first name terms with household names in the business world. They call me if they have a concern, or they want a bit of advice. 'Could we have a spot of lunch next time you're in town? There's a couple of things I'd like to run past you.' It's easy to get carried away on a wave of self-importance. I see that in my colleagues all around me and I don't want to join them.

In the midst of pondering the meaning of life, I suddenly jolt in my seat and remember that it is 'own clothes day' at the boys' primary school in aid of Comic Relief. And I have forgotten to tell our nanny, who arrives at 7.30am. She will have got them dressed in their school uniforms by the time I get a phone signal when we land. She doesn't quite get what a game of day-to-day survival I play and will be annoyed by the last-minute change.

Though I am in her good books more often than the boys' dad, whom she claims is reliably late every time it is his turn to be home by 6.30pm when she clocks off. She works four long days but has a three-day weekend. He really hates being greeted with a ticking off as he opens the front door. 'Funny how the trains always run late when it's his turn, or the roads are always busy.' It is like water off a duck's back, and the next time the same thing happens. I also remember with horror that on Friday a fancy-dress outfit is required for a class assembly. Something Greek or Roman. I ponder what household props and fancy-dress box items I can pull together to create something that will pass muster.

We do make up a bit of time flying into Heathrow, and there is an express train to Paddington waiting on the platform when I get down to the station. Things are looking up. I arrive at the London office before most of the consultants who are actually based there, which is a bit galling. I feel like I have already done a day's work by the time the 9.00am internal meeting starts. Several colleagues are late. They come in carrying takeaway cups of coffee, 'Massive queue for taxis... sorry... rush hour.' Most have country pads in Berkshire, Hampshire or beyond. Monday to Friday they stay in their London townhouses or flats, leaving the wife in the country to look after the kids and the horses.

Before the business bit starts, there's chit chat. A lot of the male consultants have nicknames, like at boarding school. Twinkle Toes, Tiddles, Dingo, Knobbles. They talk about their weekends. Pony clubs, drinks parties, golf, sports cars. The women talk amongst themselves. When the meeting is called to order, the jostling for recognition and praise starts. Everyone competes to be more important than the next person. I find it nauseating.

One of the worst culprits starts, 'Yah, yah I spoke to Ian,' (CEO of a huge high street well known, soon to implode bank) and 'We're in the frame for all their retail work. They've got incredible expansion plans that he shared with me exclusively over lunch. They think we are marvellous. I'm sure he's not even talking with any competitors. He and I are like this [puts one hand in the other and clasps it to illustrate closeness]. We just need to sit back and wait for the business to come. It's going to be a gravy train chaps.' He sits back and takes another sip of his coffee. Triumphant, like he has already delivered and done the work. 'Marvellous,' the room replies, 'well done you.' Brought up in the school of hard knocks recruitment where you take nothing for granted until 'it's over the line', I'm staggered by the arrogance and naivety.

I'm asked if I can do a pitch in Exeter, as it's outside London. Surely not even they think Exeter is in the north of England. Do they realise it will take me six hours on a good day to get there? They ham it up, 'Could be a really big strategic account. It's in a growing sector. This role is not the most exciting, but it could lead to other things.' The pitch is on Friday, my supposed day off. At the end of the meeting, the chair says, 'Jolly well done everyone. I think it is so valuable getting together like this. It really fires us all up. Marvellous. On we go.' I am shattered already.

After the meeting, I try to find a room with a VPN to sit in and plug in my computer. I go along the length of the corridor, 'No, sorry, this one is taken by the managing partner.' Followed by, 'No, sorry, these are booked for clients.' I resign myself to not being able to log on, take some printed off draft proposals and candidate reports out of my briefcase, go and sit in a quiet bit of reception and start correcting them.

When reception starts to fill up with clients and candidates, I head to the kitchen to make a drink and have a chat with one of the pearl necklace bedecked PAs. A different breed from the ones we have in Manchester, most are terribly posh and say 'Ok yah' a lot. The chairman's assistant comes in to have a word, 'How totally lovely to see you. We haven't seen you for absolutely ages. You simply must come down more often. How are things going up there in the north?' I was here only three days ago, I think wearily. I have a crisis of confidence. Perhaps I am so unremarkable that I am in fact invisible. I do the rounds of the London consultants' offices, as I am always being told it is valuable 'to network and be seen'. No one is free. Either interviewing, or on the phone. Some catch my eye and smile back at me through the windows of their office doors. Obviously 'being seen' is at their convenience, not mine.

I'm starving hungry having got up so early. Hopefully, my candidate will be on time for his interview and then I'll have an early lunch. I have mixed feelings about lunch here in the London office. It is served every day in the boardroom and symbolises everything I find difficult about the firm. The partners love the whole ritual of it. 'We have our own cook, isn't it marvellous. It's so important to get together during the day. Very civilised. Chew the cud. See what's going on. Share some market intel.'

I take the candidate down to reception having completed the interview. As I go back upstairs to the boardroom, I wonder how many hours and days of my life I have spent interviewing since I entered recruitment fifteen years ago. I take a deep breath and walk into the room. Lunch smells good. Cook is there. She always wears a pie crust stripey blue shirt, pearls and a navy skirt and lives in Putney. She usually appears quite frantic to me, talks terribly quickly and in the poshest voice you can imagine.

'What delights have you got for us today, cook?' one of the partners asks, as if we are in some grand country house. They peer into the dishes left on hotplates on the sideboard. 'Yummy. Just look at this.'

'Chicken in a creamy tarragon sauce, wild rice and some lovely fresh mangetouts straight from my own veg garden. Yah, I grow them in big pots on my roof garden. Picked them this morning before I came in. Super-duper, aren't they?'

'Oh cook, you do spoil us. Fresh mangetouts. You grow them in pots? How absolutely marvellous. You are simply wonderful cooking this lovely food for us every day. Always something different. Highlight of our day.' People help themselves as they come in and take a seat at one of the places set around the boardroom table.

I serve myself, look for a friendly face to sit next to, and start to eat. The mangetouts are indeed very fresh and taste quite unlike the ones I buy occasionally in clingfilm wrapped trays from the supermarket. I feel I have nothing to contribute to the ongoing conversation around the table. Someone reminds us again how lucky we are, 'All the other big head-hunting firms have had to dispense with their own cook. All the partners have to leave the office these days to buy a sandwich or whatever they have, which is all rather a nuisance when one is so busy and got things to do. So much nicer for us that we can just pop up to the third floor.'

The pressure mounts to say something, I cannot just sit there 'on mute'. Luckily Tiddles comes to sit next to me. We worked together previously at another firm. 'Alright?' he asks, big smile on his face. The conversation carries on around us. 'That was a great deal you did last week. Super work. Has it been announced yet? Haven't seen it in the *FT*.' We chat a little bit about our respective families. A bit of normality.

It is like being the audience to some bizarre play. I can only observe and reflect that I have little in common with what I see being played out before me. One partner shares his holiday plans to take his family to Antigua for the half term break. They have friends who have a villa out there and it will be 'a bit of a break'. He continues to hold forth, 'It's rather embarrassing because when my children get on a plane, they automatically turn to the left!' I look at Tiddles for an explanation. 'To go into business class,' he whispers, laughing.

Another is in full flow about the opera she saw last night. 'Marvellous. Simply marvellous. We had the best seats in the house. I say, are any of you going to Glyndebourne this year? It's an absolute must. Just fantastic.' Someone else is talking about the difficulties of maintaining your own swimming pool, the pump room is apparently always flooding and the man who comes to do the chemicals and fish the leaves out is unreliable. I eat lunch and as soon as it is seemly, I leave. Not that anyone would notice anyway.

My taxi is here to take me to the client meeting I have come to London for. As I wait for the lift to go down to the ground floor reception, the ghost of Grandma appears. Goodness knows what she makes of it all,

'Well, what a carry on that were. Never 'eard 'owt like it. They're not fer real, them lot. All 'em airs and graces. Ah don't know what to meke of all this jumping on and off planes and fancy goings on. It's enough to turn yer 'ead reight enough, so think on lass. Underneath, they're just like thee an' me. An' whilst ah'm about it, growin' mangetouts is like fallin' off a bike, yer granddad used to say. Note to it. So, you can tell 'cook' or 'oever she is to put that in 'er pipe and smoke it. Reckon the sooner yer out of all o' this, the better.'

As the taxi drives through the West End, I people watch through the window. It couldn't be more different than where my grandma came from. And where my dad grew up. Three generations, three different lives, but threaded together by family stories and handed down values. There are groups of visitors following guides who hold umbrellas aloft. Students in jeans and combos walk purposefully to lectures, their laptop bags hanging from their shoulders. Elegant couples in designer clothes shop. People hurry along to early lunch appointments, jostling for position on the crowded pavements. I love the vibrancy of London. Its diversity.

I wait in reception and eventually the client's PA comes down. She tells me her boss only has half an hour instead of an hour, so please can I stick to this and make sure I don't overrun. This meeting is the reason I got up before dawn, I think dejectedly. I go in. He tells me they are about to complete a big deal. I will read about it in the papers tomorrow apparently. He is stressed and distracted. I get the feeling he just wants me out as soon as possible. I take him through my work so far. He nods his head as if to hurry me up, asks a couple of questions, and says he's happy with progress. His PA sees me to the lift afterwards.

I have a taxi waiting to take me back to the office. I still feel annoyed about being 'squeezed in' but it goes with the territory. My clients are paid vast sums of money, and the personal and corporate cost of failure if they take their eye off the wrong ball at the wrong time is huge. As I get in the black cab, I hear the radio. 'News just in from New York of a blaze in the North Tower of the World Trade Centre. Early reports suggest terrorists may be responsible.' 'Blimey,' I say to the taxi driver. He turns the volume up so I can hear. By the time we get back to the office, it transpires that it was a passenger plane that caused the fire. 'It crashed straight into the tower? Deliberately?' I'm stunned and so is he. Reports then come through of a second plane crashing into the South Tower. The descriptions are horrifying. Eyewitnesses recall what happened and describe seeing people hanging out of the windows. Some have reportedly jumped to their death. Sirens wailing, people shouting and screaming. When we reach the office, I nod in thanks to the taxi driver, both of us unable to speak after what we have been listening to and enter the ground floor reception.

The security guard is glued to the TV monitor in front of him. I lean over the reception desk and watch it over his shoulder. Both towers are clearly on fire. Huge clouds of smoke billowing out. 'Oh my god. It's going,' I hear the commentator shrieking. Wordlessly, the guard and I watch first one, then the other tower crumple like a stack of play bricks and become dust. The noise is indescribable. We can only look at each other open-mouthed.

I go back upstairs. Everyone who isn't in a meeting has heard the news. People are watching replays on TV. I pack my bag and head for Paddington. I just want to be home, safe, with my family. Inevitably there is chaos at Heathrow. Security alerts and massive delays. My fellow passengers and I are all on high alert. Looking for anything out of the ordinary or suspicious. There is an eery silence as we are processed through the familiar airport security and departure routines.

As I wait at Heathrow, I reflect back to when my brother died, and the pledge I made not 'to live small'. I ask myself how successful I have been in achieving this. In my job, I have climbed to the top of the mountain. I have been made a partner. The youngest female to achieve this and I have had three children along the way. But am I happy? In reality, the view from the top is not as magnificent as I thought it would be, and the striving continues. In fact, the pressures on a partner only get greater. I look around me to the other people in the business lounge. Not one of them is smiling, and it's not just because of what is happening in New York. Furrowed brows, bags under their eyes, bodies slumped, they reach for the complimentary alcohol to anaesthetise themselves.

I look in my paper diary for what the rest of the week holds. Leeds tomorrow for an interview, then up to Newcastle for a shortlist meeting. My secretary tells me I have had a call from an Edinburgh client, so would it be possible to go on to Edinburgh after the Newcastle meeting? The following day I am back in London for a dinner, and she wonders if I could fly to Frankfurt the morning afterwards to fit that last interview in for the shortlist due in next week. And then, in amongst this, I have to make a fancy-dress outfit. Suddenly I make the decision that has been waiting to be made. I feel relief. Then fear.

January 2002 sees me turn forty and finally giving in my notice to an incredulous senior partner, 'But you've done so well. You're at the top of your game.' He is very gracious and says if I change my mind, I can come back whenever I want. He thinks I am having a mid-life crisis. My gut is telling me that I'm doing the right thing. I just want to be at home more. I don't want to look back and regret not being around my lovely boys, who are growing up so fast.

I quickly realise that I have become institutionalised by work and its rituals. When every minute of every day is accounted for, you are spared any time to think. You simply follow the schedule set out for you. The only choices to be made are micro in nature. Who would I like to have on my team for this new assignment I have won? What is the optimum way to organise my diary? Which candidates shall I shortlist? Do I have time to pop into the supermarket on the way home and still get back for the nanny on time? What is the most efficient traffic-avoiding route, so I can get one son to his piano lesson and the other two to football practice and not be too early for one thing or too late for the other?

The first day of my new-found freedom is normal for the rest of the family but totally disorientating for me. I walk with the children to school, a novelty for us all on a Monday. I come back through the village and take my time buying bread from the bakery and meat from the butchers. How strange it is not to be rushing around. Shall I have a coffee at Costas? No, that feels just too self-indulgent, and anyway what sad person has coffee by themselves at 9.15am? Everyone I see through the café window is sitting with friends, but I'm not part of the 'coffee drinking club', reserved for mothers who don't work. And nor am I anymore a proud member of the 'working mums club'. I feel like I don't belong anywhere.

I get home and tidy up, then make a drink and sit at the kitchen table. My diary and the calendar on the wall are both quite empty of commitments and appointments. It is five hours before I am required to be back at school for picking up the children. I stare into my cup of coffee for the answer to the question I can no longer avoid, 'What on earth happens now?'

CHAPTER 11

Onion (*Allium cepa*)

Onion
Allium cepa

2005–2015

Bunkbed room in holiday house

Ouch, well that hurt. And I wasn't expecting it, and certainly wasn't braced for impact. A fist has gone through the plasterboard. I've been punched out of sheer frustration. I'm the so-called bunkbed room. When they were little, they were transported up the motorway, bathed and in their pyjamas, then lifted into bed when they arrived. They used to wake up the following morning full of excitement for the adventures outside they would have. Making obstacle courses to ride their bikes around, pretending to be rock stars using old plastic barrels and sticks as their keyboards and guitars, rolling down the grass banks and latterly playing ballgames with their dog Billy. In the summer, they would swim in the outdoor pool in Greystoke and pester their mum for sweets before using up any remaining energy in the playpark there. Or go to the special place in Bowscale where they jumped into the rockpools and dried themselves on towels warmed by the sun on the slabs of stone.

That was then. But now, the eldest is a moody teenager. Spends time in here being angry about being kept from his social life in Manchester. I can understand how he feels, but it's a shame because my days with this family are numbered. I've enjoyed the last twelve years.

Friends and family coming and going. Big Christmas celebrations. I remember that year when there was a house full and the septic tank couldn't cope with all the toilet flushing and showers. Everyone had to go to the loo in the garden until after Christmas when someone came to sort it out. Elderly relatives too. Blooming freezing it was, but it added to the fun of it all. And those jamborees every summer have been a lot of fun.

Onion (*Allium cepa*)

Several families here for a weekend, usually near the longest day in June when it stays light until 11pm. A big BBQ in the evening. Children charging around taking advantage of their inebriated parents not overlooking what they were up to. Games of cricket and tents pitched on the lawn. Trips to Silloth beach for games of rounders. I've heard them talking about selling me. It's such a beautiful setting. Right by a stream, mature trees and floriferous shrubs all through the spring and summer. Only sheep for company. The only noises which interrupt the peace and tranquillity are children playing and crows building their nests. On the day they move out, the lady of the house will sit on the blue bench overlooking the back garden and the stream and she will shed a tear. As the lady of the house before her also did. Wonder who we will get next?

Determined that I wasn't going to be a helicopter mum, increasingly I had less day-to-day involvement in the older boys' lives. They spent more and more time with their friends or in their rooms. The youngest was still at junior school, but even he was striding out, saying he didn't need (want) me to walk to school with him anymore. Having been the centre of their worlds, I moved to the periphery, where I combined observing them from a respectful distance whilst choosing which battles to fight.

Occasionally I was invited into their lives, sometimes being given more detail than I wanted. Teenage years tested me sorely. The mood swings. The sound of slamming doors reverberating through the house when I said the wrong thing, or my patience had been exhausted. Then, when I least expected it, the occasional 'you're still my friend' hug and a ruffle of my hair. We muddled along sometimes better than others.

I played tennis with each of the boys at the club we belonged to down the road. When I was feeling particularly brave, we played doubles. Inevitably it was highly competitive, with arguments about line calls and who was the best player. They were physically strong and, after lessons with the coach, could hit the ball hard and with good technique. It was either impossible to get their shots back because they came over the net with such ferocity, or they sent the ball clean over the perimeter fence into a neighbouring garden, never to be seen again.

But I could beat them all at singles, which confounded them, 'Mum, you're so not the best player. We are much better than you. The only reason you win is because you're so, well, so boring. You just keep getting the ball in and make fewer mistakes than us.' To which I routinely replied, 'That's actually the way it works. It's the person that gets the most points that wins.' They would jointly shake their heads, 'It's just not fair. You don't deserve to win. It's properly annoying.' They were, however, keen to partner me in the club handicapped mixed doubles and we typically got through a couple of preliminary rounds before the errors cost us too dear.

During this time, the boys also honed their arguing skills. Testosterone fuelled, they locked horns with their father about pretty much anything, but they would also delight in finding my weak spots and use them to wind me up. The classic was an assertion that women's prize money at Wimbledon should not be the same as men's, because they played fewer sets and therefore provided less entertainment.

Onion (*Allium cepa*)

I couldn't help but be drawn into the futile debate, even though it always followed the same old course and left me feeling frustrated and furious.

Relieved of the burden of corporate life, I now carried the weight of working out what the next phase in my life would be. In the meantime, I became the person that cooked meals and kept everything together. I regarded their rooms as their territory, only threatening to go in with a black plastic rubbish sack if they didn't clear their 'floordrobes', which had clean and dirty laundry indiscriminately mixed together, with other detritus, some unmentionable, hidden amongst it.

Generally, they stayed out of trouble, the odd police caution for mildly anti-social behaviour or trespass excepted. Inevitably, the devil that is alcohol encroached on all our lives. 'Stop fussing Mum, we're not stupid,' they said as I encouraged drinking a pint of milk before going out, to line their stomachs. And one by one, we had the inevitable excess vodka incidents where they were brought home, insensible. For their dad it was a rite of passage, almost something to be celebrated. For me, it was horrifying. In those moments they seemed so vulnerable, and it reminded me of how fragile life is.

The only time I was ever put on any kind of permanent raised pedestal was when I went to court as a magistrate and listened to a procession of sad stories. Being called Ma'am was a pleasant change from the not so formal salutations I got in the house. It was a levelling experience: the professional woman we found guilty of stealing from her employer; an old lady, for the second time, who knew she would be sent to jail, and so did a runner from the courtroom;

the teenager betrayed by a youth worker at his children's home, who reported him for breaching his ASBO when he could have asked him to come inside the building and remain on the right side of the law; the well-off businessman who escaped multiple speeding convictions and losing his licence by hiring the lawyer who could always find a loophole.

I had driven myself half crazy for months trying to figure out my next career move, when an ex-colleague dropped by one sunny day with her new baby. We had lunch in the garden. She said her contacts in the States were talking about this new thing called 'coaching' and she thought my combination of people skills and understanding of corporate life would make me a good fit for it.

My first coaching course in London attracted the usual mix of serious minded 'suits' and pink-haired crystal reading new age women. I loved the realness and the humanity of the work. It was like trying on a new pair of shoes that fitted perfectly from the first time of wearing. We are all like onions, we were told, with tough outer layers that we come to rely on for protection against the world. Rarely do we give any thought as to what lies underneath. Coaching in essence is about carefully and respectfully helping people to remove the outer layers so they can move forwards more purposefully.

One day I am coaching the CEO of a small charity. I have a comfortable office at home, and we are midway through the two-hour session. There is an unexpected knock at the door. Embarrassed at the disruption, I excuse myself and go to see who is there. The postman has already been, and we rarely get any visitors at this time of day. It is Margaret, our next-door neighbour who is always on the ball regarding what is going on in the neighbourhood.

She knew the previous occupants of our house well. Apparently, they were party animals and she told us many lurid tales of the swingers' activities that went on before our time. This view is supported by the collage of 'adult' cut-out glossy pictures on the wall behind the red painted bar in the dark basement room. It's where the children now play hide and seek and murder in the dark. Margaret looks like she has something important to tell me.

'I'm sorry to interrupt, I know you have a client with you because I saw him arrive. But it's Basil [our cat]. I think he's dead.'

I look to where she is pointing on the drive, and sure enough there is a black and white cat who looks like he literally dropped dead as he was walking across it. I run back upstairs and explain this unfortunate occurrence to my client, who leaves immediately, passing the prostrate Basil on the driveway. I call Stephen in the office as I am unsure of the etiquette of handling dead cats. He comes home and reassures me that before leaving the office he researched 'how to bury a cat' on the internet. We wrap him in a towel and put him in the bike shed. I want the children to be there when we bury him.

I pick the children up from school and tell them the sorry story. We go to the local garden centre and find a model of a cat which is suitable for outside. We paint it to look like Basil and then wait for Stephen to get home to begin the burial. He duly arrives and gets his spade out of the shed. A man on a mission, he digs and digs, saying he doesn't want a fox to be able to unearth the poor cat. I ask him to keep his voice down. It's not an image I want the boys to have in their heads. But he's busy at work, wants to get the job done with the minimum of fuss, and is in no mood for paying attention to the emotional impact of losing a much-loved family pet.

For my part, I have a different agenda. My coaching head and maternal instinct tell me that this is the first time they have known anyone or anything to die, and I want them to say their farewells, feel sad and know it is an integral part of life. Inevitably it goes horribly wrong. I call the boys to come outside and say it's time to say goodbye to Basil and we all stand round the big hole, with one of them clutching the painted black and white model. Without a bye or leave, Stephen brings the cat out of the shed, removes the towel around him, and throws his now stiff body into the bottom of the hole, 'Well we don't want to waste the towel, do we?' The youngest is freaked out by the black and white fur hitting the earth and runs screaming into the house. The older boys look a bit shellshocked and stand back from the hole. I am handed back the model we carefully painted, 'Here Mum, you put it on the grave when it's finished. We're going inside.'

After getting a few hundred practitioner hours under my belt, and completing another coaching qualification, I enrol on a two-year programme. It's based in Denver. I'll be eligible for the highest-level professional accreditation if successful and will be one of only twenty to hold it in the UK. I am excited to be going out for the first of three training weeks taking place in the States. An adventure.

'Will you have us hugging trees when you get back?' asked one client nervously when I told him I was off to Arizona to learn some 'new-fangled' stuff. I check in to my hotel late at night just after landing. Jet lag means I wake up ridiculously early, but then I discover the pool opens at 4.00am so I find my costume in my still unpacked bag and take advantage of the early start. I do my 100 lengths and am back in my room an hour later.

I look out of the window. The sun is just starting to rise over Denver, and I can see the mountains in the far distance. Everything is vast. Like my hotel room which has two king sized beds in it. The downtown business district with its dozens of skyscrapers sits in a dip. Freeways bend around them and disappear towards the horizon. Outside the hotel is a ten lane super-highway with motels and restaurants on either side.

I go down for breakfast and sit down in the vast dining room. 'Morning, ma'am. What can I get you? Tea or coffee. And help yourself to the buffet. It's right over there. Have a good day.' I go over and look. I think to myself how my boys would love this. The perfect breakfast in their eyes with as many waffles and pancakes with sticky maple syrup as you can eat. We were once delayed overnight in Denmark on the way back from a skiing holiday in Norway, where we had stayed in a very lovely hotel which served the breakfasts of your dreams. Every imaginable kind of ham, cheese, fish, nuts, fresh and dried fruit, bread, yoghurt, juice, coffee. The budget hotel near Copenhagen airport where we were put up overnight had processed cheese slices, white bread and a waffle maker. 'Yes, at last a decent breakfast,' they chorused as they saw the buffet.

My attention turning to the day ahead, I take my usual yoghurt and fruit and return to the table where someone is now sitting opposite my place. 'Mind if I join you?' Shortly, along comes another couple of people to fill the table and we all introduce ourselves. Two are from the US and one from Ireland.

I start to share my morning thus far. 'To share' is a verb much used amongst the coaching fraternity, along with 'to sense', 'to reflect', 'to be mindful', 'to feel', 'to empower', 'to embody'. I tell them I woke early and couldn't sleep, so checked and saw the swimming pool opened at 4am, normal in the US apparently. I go on to say that I swam 100 lengths. For a bit of colour, I add, 'It was so therapeutic, just following the blue line at the bottom of the pool, not having to think about anything else.'

As soon as I have said this, I look up expectantly. I am amongst coaches and some can't resist beginning the competition to be 'most coach-like'. Three appraising pairs of eyes suddenly upon me. 'Interesting...' one of them says and just looks at me. The second one narrows his eyes, leans back and takes the whole of me in, as if to say, 'Yes, that tells me all I need to know about you.' The third one leans forward and says, 'So what do we think this thin blue line tells us about our new friend?' And to me directly, now warming to his theme and his audience, 'And how would it be for you if there was no thin blue line? What would that feel like?' and then leans back very self-satisfied as if he has said the most profound thing in the world.

It's been quite a performance getting ready to come away. The boys are a bit older now, and my mum has said she will come over one evening and cook for everyone.

'How will Stephen manage when you're away in America? He's got so much on already, and those boys are a full-time job. Tell him, we will help him out,' she said on the phone just before I left for the airport.

'He is perfectly able to do it and it's not often he's left in charge,' I say briskly.

I phoned him last night after checking in. After the pleasantries, I say, 'I've just remembered that it's a school trip on Thursday and you need to provide a packed lunch, wellington boots and waterproofs.' I am secretly delighted to miss this task, as it's always a minefield. Either the drink is 'the wrong drink' or the 'crisps are boring and not like everyone else has', or the 'bread is too thickly sliced or not the right kind'. And that's before you get on to the vexed subject of spending money, and whether whatever the amount is 'should count as part of weekly pocket money or is in addition to it'. Allowances are in any event a major bone of contention. Their dad believes they should get jobs, to understand the value of money, and says I am soft. For my part, I want to give them some of the things that were denied to me as a child. We generally finish up with a slightly messy compromise.

'Don't fuss, I am told, I'll do it. Making a packed lunch is no big deal. You just concentrate on your course. It will be fine. Love you. Must go now as we're late.'

After breakfast, I gather my things and go up to the conference suite on the top floor. The bell rings, conversations are quickly ended and we all take a badge before taking our places in the circle. There are three course leaders. They sit in a row. The first one to speak is an elegant woman, maybe about forty, wrapped in a cashmere shawl that she pulls around her expansively, then opens and repulls around her. She is like an actress opening a play. We are spellbound.

'So...' a long-drawn-out sound, and then she stops and nods her head towards the circle. She takes three deep theatrical breaths, looks around the assembled group, about twenty-five of us, takes each of us in in a way that makes you feel she already knows you. She gazes round the circle two or three times, smiling if she catches your eye. I weakly smile back but instantly feel a bit silly. Finally, after an age, she looks up, smiles, pauses, and says, 'Welcome'. And puts her hands together as if in prayer. We all mumble something back. Some do the prayer thing back. After some initial reluctance, on about Day Two, I join in and put my hands together in acknowledgment of what is happening in the room. I'll be doing it when I get home in the unlikely event anyone thanks me for their tea.

After a couple of days, I call home. I'm missing the kids but not in the same way I did when I was a head-hunter staying in my luxury suite in Phoenix and finally decided to bow out of corporate life. I know when I get home I will have loads of time with them, because I'm self-employed so can arrange my diary to make sure I do.

When I call home, I hold the phone out at the side of my

head to dim the hullaballoo. A boy is screaming in the background, hysterically.

'Hi darling. Can you hear him? He's making such a fuss about his picnic lunch for his trip. He wants one of those disgusting cheese dips with mini bread sticks. I found some stuff in the fridge and made some perfectly acceptable sandwiches, but he says it's not a proper packed lunch without a bag of Frazzles or a fizzy drink. What are Frazzles anyway? And he says you normally give them a pound for spending money on school trips. Seems an awful lot. How are things with you?'

I don't want to sound as if I'm having too much fun. 'All good. The course is hard work but I'm enjoying it.' I hear the youngest saying he wants to speak with me. He grabs the phone from his dad.

'Mum, I'm convinced that the bread lady at the market is after Dad.'

The bread lady takes a stall in the middle of the covered market every Saturday. Stephen goes there and usually takes Tim with him. She has a hairy moustache and thick black hair. She sells focaccia and ciabatta and soda bread.

'After Dad has chosen his bread, she told him she had made some nice pesto, just for him and would he like some. She was definitely flirting. Then she asked where his wife was. But I jumped in and told her you are in America, but you're coming back in a few days' time. When are you coming home?'

'Thank you darling,' I say, 'two more sleeps and I'll be back.'

On the final day of the course, we are encouraged to

commune with nature outside. 'Here comes the tree hugging,' I smile to myself. We stop and listen, really listen and I am struck by how rarely my mind is totally quiet, if ever. We imagine any thoughts running through our heads as logs floating down a river, here one minute, gone the next. I'm loving the peacefulness and get wrapped up in the immediacy of the moment. I think of those frantically busy people I work with back at home. How alien this would all be for them. But how valuable if I can find a way of introducing it into my work with them.

I don't even feel the creeping sense of doom as it comes round to my turn to say something pithy in the closing circle. I find myself doing the 'prayer hands thing' to the other members of the group and the facilitators and really meaning it. I am grateful for their insights and for the learning and the company. I'm already looking forward to the second part of the course, here again in Denver in three months' time. This feels like a great community of people to be working remotely with in the next few weeks before meeting again.

And now I'm looking forward to going back to the chaos that is home. I get home on schedule via New York. The plane lands before daylight. There are few other arrivals and I whizz though passport control and collect my bag from the conveyor belt in record time. I always dread asking a waiting taxi driver to be taken to Altrincham because it's only a short journey and he's probably been waiting ages in the wee small hours for a job. He drops me off without a single word. I'm on a high from my course, so I still give him a tip. I put my key into the lock as quietly as I can. I'm hoping to sneak in, put my bags down and crawl into bed next to my sleeping husband for a bit of shut eye before everyone gets up.

As I come into the hallway, the gorgeous face of my middle son looks over the bannisters, 'Mum… you're home!' I look up and put my finger over my lips, 'Shhhh don't wake everyone up.' But I abandon all possibility of getting some sleep. He runs down the stairs and hugs me. We make breakfast and chat, then sit together and watch TV because I'm so tired I can't do anything else. Soon, more noise is coming from upstairs. The sound of the two other boys stumbling about. One of them remembers I should be home by now. He calls over the bannister. 'Mum, you home yet?' 'Yes darling,' I say, 'I'm here.' Then a while later, 'Mum, he's been in the bathroom for ages. It's not fair. Can you tell him to come out?'

I can hear their dad upstairs moving out of the shower and into the bedroom. 'Hello,' he calls over the bannister. 'One minute and I'm there.' He comes down, gives me a hug, and then eats a bowl of muesli. 'So nice to see you darling. Good flight? I've got to go now. Busy day. Good to have you back. Let's have a proper catch up later.'

A bit of absence is a good thing. I ask them what they have been up to in the six days since I saw them. 'Errrr,' one looks upwards for inspiration. 'Got picked for football team on Saturday. Got loads of homework. The usual really. Dad tried his best, but we've had some pretty random scran.' Then another chimes in, 'Matt nicked my football shorts without asking and borrowed my boots and hasn't returned them. And he got a detention, didn't you Matt?' I put my hand up for calm, 'Shall we do pancakes after school tonight? Then we can have a proper catch up,' I say optimistically.

We move to Bowdon, closer to the Metro station with its trains into Manchester and to the boys' secondary school. I have an office in a beautifully sunny light room at the front of the house. At only eight weeks old, Billy comes into our lives. He was the one who chose us when we went to see the litter of flat coat retrievers. He introduces us to the daily dog walking ritual at the Devisdale, where Cheshire's finest pooches are paraded by their Hunter welly wearing owners. Our dog proves more resistant to training than we had hoped, and most days we crawl through thickets to get him back after he rushes off in pursuit of food or a female.

For the first time in my life, I can say that I love what I do. The work is intimate and privileged. I see the best and worst of human nature. My view will always be that those with the most powerful voices, whether it be in organisations or in life generally, also carry the greatest responsibility to use them for the greater good. Working alongside individuals who commit to doing this is a huge privilege. Conversely, it is frustrating to come across leaders whose impact could be so much more positive if they were open to learning.

I pitched for some work with a CEO whom I had met once before, but he didn't remember. On the second occasion, I was shown again into his office, then left for nearly half an hour before he appeared. He finally arrived and without apology started talking,

'Your name has been given to me. I've asked around and people say good things about you, but I'm worried you're too nice.'

I was somewhat taken aback by his directness. But one of the things I learnt over the years of working with Type A personalities is that you have to give as good as you get. 'I may be gently spoken, but I don't pull my punches,' I retort. 'Why are you thinking about working with a coach?'

'I'm doing a good job here. Things are going really well. If you look at the financial results, you will see they speak for themselves, but it's my chair who thinks I might benefit from coaching.'

'What do you think?'

'Well, of course, I am open to learning, obviously I am. But I'm not sure what benefits it will give me. I'm very busy, you understand. Time is money.'

'I see. In the spirit of not pulling my punches, can I give you some feedback?'

'Yes of course.'

'I can only speak as I find. I have met you once before, here in this office. You obviously don't recall the occasion. After the meeting finished, you walked out of the room and left me in it. I assumed you were coming back, but after a while I realised you weren't, so let myself out of the building. This time, you kept me waiting for half an hour and didn't apologise. Neither of these is wrong. But I wonder if you have paused to reflect what impression this gives of you? That maybe you don't value others' time as you value your own, or even worse that you do not think or care about your impact on others? And so, I also wonder about your leadership style and whether the way you go about things always gets the best out of your people.'

I didn't get the coaching job. Not for the first time I raged about my quiet competence and gentle manner being interpreted as weaknesses. On the contrary, for this kind of work it was my secret weapon, but many leaders only hired coaches with similar styles to their own. It was less threatening that way.

Conversely, I worked with several incredibly talented women who had missed out on promotion because they were uncomfortable 'having to sell' themselves in processes that required it. When I first met them, they were unable even to own their own space, often entering the meeting room with their heads down and barely able to meet my gaze. Exhausted by working all hours in a competitive system which seemed to benefit their male counterparts, it was like this latest setback had knocked the stuffing out of them. Often these women were of an age where they had young children and were desperately trying to juggle the demands of home and work. Failing to achieve their professional goals felt doubly hard having sacrificed so much.

Being able to tell their stories without censor or fear of judgement was the beginning of coming back stronger. We worked together to re-frame the promotion process as an opportunity to showcase what they felt good about. A simple sequence of questions like, 'What are you most proud of?' followed up with 'and how were you able to achieve that?' followed by, 'What do your team and the people around you most appreciate about you?' started to give them a narrative they could both believe in and deliver with conviction.

For many women, the thought of networking with those

who have power and influence is an anathema. To them, making connections without any useful purpose in mind save their own self-promotion feels intolerable. This is further exacerbated as they observe their male counterparts successfully doing precisely the thing that they cannot bring themselves to do. But what if there was a meaningful reason to seek out more senior people whom they wouldn't normally come into contact with? Perhaps asking for sponsorship of an important project, or seeking advice, or requesting an introduction to one of their contacts. Suddenly they were not networking with senior people for their own advancement, but in support of an important work issue.

I noticed subtle changes as they began to connect with their own achievements and place in the organisation. They would hold themselves differently, stand more upright and even start to make subtle changes to their wardrobes. One said to me, 'I'm going to wear a red dress for the promotion board. I feel like I want to stand out, not blend into the background like I have always preferred to do.'

Often, I would hear the words, 'I've never admitted that to anyone before,' or 'Thank you for letting me put words to something I have always known but not acknowledged.' And occasionally, 'This has been the best development I have ever had. It has been a game changer for me.'

And then, always looking for the next challenge, I decided to move onto working with teams and boards of directors. After all, it was the next logical step, and meant I could continue to develop my skills and get my head around the highly complex dynamics that happen in groups and organisations. After all, I couldn't rest on my laurels and needed to keep stretching myself, pushing ahead.

Wastepaper bin in home office

She learnt lots of new stuff on her latest course. Thought I'd give it a go myself and become the inanimate object that observes and gives a new perspective. I see her sitting at her computer until late at night writing workshops for teams. Standing by the flipchart, she agonises over getting the exercises exactly right. She seems less confident than when she is working with individuals. I suppose this is newer for her and it's less straightforward to strip away the layers of the onion when you're dealing with lots of people.

'Working with teams is like wading through treacle,' I have heard her say on the phone. She has piles of textbooks that she reads and rereads. There are reams of paper in me, discarded ideas, and reports that get written then amended then amended yet again. She enjoys the intellectual challenge of the work, but she misses knowing that she has made a tangible difference. The results are not so immediate, and there is less appreciation. Team bosses with a lot at stake. They want answers and results quickly, and this work requires their patience. Months if not years of quiet application. Two steps forward, one step back. She reflects long and hard about the impact of the work so far and the best next steps. And everything must be managed on a tight budget. Writing, then re-writing programmes of work, all for sometimes only half a day spent working with the team. Then long debriefs with the boss afterwards. She looks stressed by it, like she is no longer loving the work.

Onion (*Allium cepa*)

I realised I had a choice and didn't have to strive and 'conquer' things just because they were difficult and there to be overcome. 'Just because I can, I don't have to,' is a mantra I carried forward. But I also started to think more and more about finding my own voice, rather than helping others to find theirs. As a mum at times, I feel invisible: the one who makes things possible for everyone else. My early working life was spent helping those with louder voices than my own to move their careers forwards by finding them a new and better job. My coaching work is all about being the invisible supporter. In fact, the better I am at it, the more invisible I should be. Increasingly there's a voice inside me that urges me to come out of the wings and move onto centre stage. I find the thought terrifying.

CHAPTER 12

Pea (*Pisum sativum*)

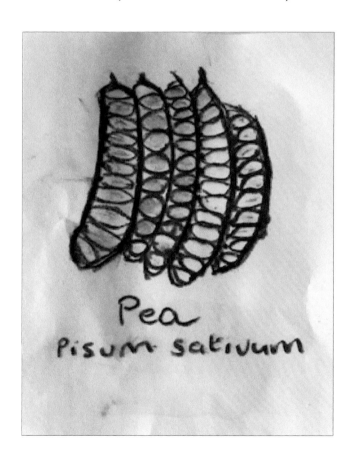

1979

'Oh my God, Norman. I don't believe it. She can't have passed her driving test first time. Do you know, she passes everything first time, that one? Unbelievable. It's only the morning, but I think I need a sherry.' This is Mum's reaction when I ring Dad to tell him my good news. It's not quite what I'd expected or hoped.

To be fair, I was not the most natural learner driver in history. When Dad was teaching me, I never seemed to get the hang of the clutch control. He would calmly sit there as I stalled the car yet again. 'Your dad has the patience of a saint,' my mum would say, 'shame driving lessons are so expensive.'

The worst incident was when we were driving home from school, chatting away and I misjudged the driveway, a sharp left turn from the road. I barely heard my dad, 'Careful! You're going a bit too fast,' and before I can do anything to correct things, I took one of the gate hinges clean off, along with the side of the car.

But all in all, I deserve to pass, I say to myself. I bet they won't complain when I give them a lift home from the pub. Or I collect my brother and sister and save them a trip out. No, they are not going to rain on my parade.

I walk away from the driving test centre towards the fish and chip café where I work as a waitress. I have on my new black and red stripey T-shirt that I bought with some of my wages. I'm feeling pleased with myself. Skegness seems like a metropolis at the side of the small village where I live. Even the amusement arcades seem vibrant and exciting.

The takeaways and coffee shops are getting ready to open. I hear scraping noises as stacks of plastic chairs and tables are being dragged out onto the pavements. Delivery vans are parked everywhere, unloading plastic crates full of hamburger buns, frozen chips, sliced bread and great big tubs of margarine. I wave to a girl I know from school who works in one of the greasy spoon caffs, as my parents call them, and is sitting in the window folding paper napkins carelessly.

It's only 10.30am and I don't have to be at work for another twenty minutes, so I pop into Woolworths. I look through the records. I like Donny Osmond and David Cassidy. Not keen on Michael Jackson. In the end I don't choose anything. Just knowing I could buy them feels enough of a treat. I flick through the hair accessories on the rotating stand. I'd quite like one of those fancy engraved hair slides that everyone is wearing. But when I put it in my hair, Mum will say it looks silly and reminds her of my Grandma Farmer who has worn a slide for as long as I can remember. Trying to explain to Mum that it's the fashion would only make her eyes roll.

Grandma has become a figure of fun in our family. When we visit, we get to hear her long list of aches and pains. She spends most of her time lying on a couch 'resting'. We imitate the priceless 'grandma phrases' behind her back and stifle our giggles when she comes out with one. I can hear her funny sayings so clearly sometimes; it is like she is in the same room as me.

When I come out of Woolworths, I see ahead the line of donkeys wearily wending their way to the beach. I know how they feel. Nearly there, I round the corner, pass the wooden hut selling candy floss and walk across the road. Staff use the storeroom door. I turn the handle and push my shoulder against it, adjusting my eyes to the darkness. I pass the sacks of potatoes, go through the long thin kitchen, then make my entrance into the café using the left-hand windowless swing door.

The café double swing doors

Well, it's a strange old life. We get kicked countless times a day, but we are the nerve centre of the whole operation. All day long the plates of food come in one door, and the washing up goes back through the other. We never stop. Our gaffe is not classy but it's home. We've been here since the old car showroom was converted five years ago. So much glass. When the sun shines it's boiling. No one thought about that did they? On Sundays and bank holidays, queues of people snake around the outside, back towards the coach station. The punters are mainly from the Midlands. Dreadful accent, but they're harmless enough. Behind us is the kitchen, a gloomy affair with no natural light. It leads into the takeaway where the food is fried. Through the kitchen is the storeroom.

Nina is the manageress of the café. She would be quite attractive if she didn't wear all that black eyeliner. Looks like something out of a horror film. She's had a late night. Not a lot of organising going on so far today. The waitresses all wear cheap and nasty blue nylon overalls with buttons down the front. There are usually eight of them. It's nearly opening time and judging by the number of people around, it's going to be nonstop. Still, look on the bright side, only six hours till closing time.

The new girl has taken her driving test this morning. I wonder if she has passed. Oh, here she comes. She looks pleased with herself.

Pea (*Pisum sativum*)

I am bursting to tell everyone my news. 'I passed,' I blurt out, arms aloft. Big smile. 'I knew you would. You're so jammy. You pass everything. Did you get the old smelly examiner?' my friend asks all at one and is not quite as delighted for me as I hoped. Undeterred, I carry on brightly. 'How is everyone?' They yawn, 'Tired. We went out last night. Finished up at the Winter Gardens. There was some music on, and we stayed out until 1.00am.'

I'm not that sympathetic. 'Have you decided who is having which tables today?' I say to Nina brightly. 'Not yet. Feeling a bit bleary to be honest. Which ones do you want?' she asks wearily. Blimey, it must be my lucky day. Not only have I passed my driving test, but now she's asking me which tables I want. 'I'll have the four by the window please,' I say as matter-of-factly as I can. 'Ok, you can have them,' Nina says, grabbing the bunch of keys from underneath the till and moving towards the entrance double doors, 'I don't have the energy to argue about it today.'

The café double swing doors

Well, she looks like the cat that got the cream alright. Whoever gets the four tables by the window generally goes home with the most tips. They all get to keep the tips left on their tables, so that's why it matters. It's alright for them but what about us? What do we get for doing a good job? Sweet FA. Still, we should get some happy punters today. It's fine and sunny but not too hot. And hopefully, the waitresses won't get too stressy. We like to be the only drama queens around here. Ok deep breath, she's unlocking the doors. In they come. Smile.

Once the café is open, my tables fill up first. Like they normally do. I feel for my notepad in my pocket, check my hair is tidy, put on my best smile and go across to take the first order. 'Hello, my lovely,' one of the customers in a mac and headscarf says, 'We'd like a pot of tea for four, not too strong mind, with a jug of hot water on the side and some nice fresh milk.' My heart sinks. Not a promising start. 'I'm afraid we don't do pots of tea. We only do cups of tea, but I can make them just how you like.' She is indignant, 'What, no pots of tea? You're joking aren't you lovely? Don't they have pots of tea in Skegness? Oh, I do prefer a proper pot. Never the same with just a teabag.'

They finally accept there is no teapot option and I get their individual cups of tea ready. But as I come back through the swing doors, balancing my trayful, the liquid spills over into all the saucers. I arrive at the table a bit stressed. They all look disappointedly at the saucers swimming in tea and then up at me. 'Don't worry love, we'll put the tea back in the cups,' they mutter and shake their heads, 'young girls, they've got no idea.'

I go to the next table. 'Hello. What can I get for you all?' This lot seem nice but a bit dippy. 'What have you got love?' They look up at me somewhat confused. 'There's no menus on the tables, so we don't know what you've got.'

I point to the enormous menu on the wall. 'Everything is on the board. All the food is cooked freshly. Can I get you some drinks whilst you make your minds up?' I need to move this along a bit, as my other tables are looking at me in a 'when you've got a minute love, we'd like some service please' kind of way. I dither between trying to hurry this first lot along or just leaving them whilst they ponder.

But before I can decide, one of them asks, 'Can you tell me how big the haddocks are love? I like a nice piece of haddock, but I don't like them if they're too big. Overfaces me, you see love. And I don't like waste. Maybe I should have a bit of cod. But we had cod pie the other day.' And then she notices we've got plaice too. 'Well now I'm all of a dither. No, I think I'll stick with my first thought and have a bit of haddock.'

After much diplomacy, going backwards and forwards between my tables, I finally get two complete food orders and am in such a hurry to get through the swing doors, I almost bump into a woman with a pushchair who's just come in and is looking for a table. She's asking Nina if she can sit on one of my tables by the window as there's more space there for the pushchair. Nina confirms that, as she can see, they are all full, and points to the far end of the café. 'How about going up there where it's less crowded?' But the woman is determined. 'I'll just wait here, until one of them comes free.' I hear all of this going on as I kick open the swing door on the left and go into the takeaway section to get my orders. The door makes a satisfying 'thump' followed by the swish as it closes.

The café double swing doors

Well, there's always one. There'll be trouble with that woman with the pushchair, mark my words. It's manic in here already today. Hopefully, it will quieten down later and we'll get the latest gossip. When they're not busy, the waitresses bitch about each other and swap stories of who's got off with who and who would like to get off with who. Brightens up the day. And they like to have a bit of a laugh, usually at the customers' expense. They have this competition as to how many plates they can balance on the crook of their arms as they kick us open with one foot and quickly shoot through before we slam shut behind them.

'Two cod, three haddock, one plaice, one steak pie and one sausage,' I shout as I run in to where the fryers are. 'Coming up. Busy in there?' my boss asks, wiping the sweat from his brow. 'Yes, getting busy. My tables have all filled up at once.' I lay out eight plates on the aluminium ledge. I put chips on them all and then a steak pie and a sausage on two of the plates. I stand by the fryer waiting for the fish to be cooked.

The only thing I don't like about this job is that when I get home, my brother and sister will hold their noses theatrically and say 'pooh, you stink'. After the golden fish are taken out with the big metal spatula, each meal is completed. Eight plates would be the most I have managed to carry all at the same time. Mary, who has worked here three years on the trot, holds the record with nine. 'Manage those?' my boss says, smiling. 'Think so,' I reply, concentrating on stacking them as best I can along my extended arm.

The café double swing doors

What is she thinking about? This is going to end in tears, trust us. Watch out for that sausage on the bottom plate.

I manage to get all eight plates arranged so I can take them through to the café in one go. As I make my way towards the left-hand swing door, I can feel a chip starting to burn the inside of my lower arm. But I'm committed now. Too late to go back. I kick the door open and rush into the café. The pain is getting too much to bear and I run towards the first of my tables. As the momentum builds, the sausage on the bottom plate shoots over the edge and into the pushchair of the waiting woman. It lands on top of the blue blanket of the sleeping baby. Presumably, it's a boy is my first thought.

I reach the nearest table and bend over it. The astonished customers, still recovering from the sight of the flying sausage, wordlessly help take the plates out of my arms. The waitresses standing by the till are killing themselves laughing at this spectacle. I go up to the mother of the baby and apologise profusely. 'Oh, I'm so sorry.' I don't know what else to say. I giggle when I'm nervous, so I bite my lip to stifle it. She is not very amused and ticks me off, 'You need to be more careful in future young lady. That could have caused a nasty accident. Trying to carry all those plates at once is guaranteed to end in disaster. What do you think you're doing?' She gives the baby a cursory look, but he is still soundly asleep.

The café double swing doors

Well, that was predictable. Where does she think she is? Acting out a scene in a farce? Whatever next? Oh, I don't believe it. She's picking up the sausage from the pushchair. Now what's she going to do with it? She's dropping it into her pocket, that's what. Oh my word, the look on the customers' faces. I need a brandy. She rushes into the kitchen, puts the sausage into the bin and collects another one, as cool as you like. She's taking it to its owner now, who is looking on in stunned silence. In all my five years, I haven't seen anything quite like it.

With no prospect of any tips, I take solace in the fizzy drinks machine that we have unlimited use of. Feels unbelievably decadent coming from a family where there are only such treats at Christmas or maybe birthdays. My personal favourite is a mix of lemonade and coca cola. As I sip my drink, I replay the whole scene in my head. As I do so, one of my grandma's pearls of wisdom runs through my head, 'Pet, well that were a carry on weren't it? Yer've got yersen all mithered. Relax, would ye? It'll be reight.'

I pull myself together and manage to get through the next hour and a half without incident. When I next see the boss, he grins and asks, 'Did you manage that pile of plates ok?' I reply, 'Kind of. There was a bit of a sausage incident, but it seems to have passed now.' He laughs. When Nina comes over to ask me if want to go for an early lunch, she can still barely conceal her smirks. I'm hungry after my action-packed morning, so accept gratefully and go back to the kitchen through the swing door.

I take my polystyrene food tray, stand in front of the fryer and contemplate what I want for lunch. There is some nice fried haddock just come out, so I take a piece. I then ladle two big dollops of mushy peas over the top. I give the bottle of vinegar a good shake over everything, and then douse it in salt. I pick up a wooden fork and take my food to the kitchen where I sit and lick my wounds. The lad who peels the potatoes is there having a fag. 'Had a good morning?' he asks. I think about his question. 'Well, it started off well. Passed my driving test, but it's gone downhill ever since.'

Pea (*Pisum sativum*)

The café double swing doors

Here comes the boss's wife. She's here to bring the wages and take the invoices that need paying. Totally immaculate as always, she looks out of place standing next to the kitchen waste bin. Classy, tailored royal blue skirt and matching cardigan. Cost a bob or two, I bet. She wipes her finger over the kitchen counter and raises her eyebrow. 'Everything could do with a jolly good clean and a bit of bleach. Some elbow grease, that's what's needed. These girls just waft a dishcloth at a surface and expect it to come up shining,' she complains to her husband who's just finished frying a batch of cod and has come in for a smoke. He nods to shut her up, sits on the stool next to the hot water boiler and takes a deep drag on his cigarette.

The boss's wife has come in and is having a rant about the state of the kitchen. Good time to finish lunch and return to the café. In the afternoon, things start to improve. One nice old man beckons over to me after I give him his change. 'We'd like to leave something for you my dear. Do you know, you remind us of our granddaughter? You've served us so nicely. Could you change this ten-pound note for a five and five one pounds?' As I am opening the till, Nina arrives and says to me, 'Bet you won't be so keen for those tables again, will you?' But I am no longer downcast. 'I think I'm about to get my best tip of the day,' I crow.

I go home on the bus, feeling that on balance it has been a pretty good day. Dad collects me from the bus stop and drives me home. I'm still feeling pretty chipper as I walk through the front door. I wait for the congratulations to pour in, like some movie star at the Oscar ceremony. I get changed and we all sit down to tea.

I might even tell them all the sausage story, but I haven't even managed my first forkful of steak pie when the erstwhile comedy duo kicks off. 'Well come on then, tell us. How on earth did you pass your driving test? I've been thinking about it all day.' 'You must have bribed the examiner,' my mum laughs. My dad joins in, 'No, it was just that tight top she was wearing. Never does any harm to distract your examiner.' Then my brother and sister have to get involved, 'Yes, you only passed because you were wearing that new top. You're a rubbish driver. You even managed to take the hinge off the gatepost.'

And this narrative will stand the test of time. Fast forward to when my three boys will all be desperate to get their driving licences. There will be so many 'learning to drive' stories to recount. But as soon as I start to make any observation about the number of driving tests taken and failed, or cars scratched or written off, or clutches burned out, or tyres burst on raised kerbs, or sub-standard techniques for parallel parking or reversing round corners, I will be instantly silenced by them, 'Well Grandad says you only passed your test first time because you had a tight stripey T-shirt on.'

I eat my tea as the enemy shots ring around my head. I attempt a counter-attack, 'You weren't there, so how do you all know? Anyway, can I borrow the car tonight? I'd like to go and see Dawn.' My mum almost chokes on her mouthful. She looks pleadingly at my dad, willing him to turn down my request. But instead, he says, 'Well, she has to drive by herself for the first time sometime.' We finish tea and I have to help with the washing up, as if I haven't seen enough dirty plates today already.

I bagsy doing the washing. I put everything in the sink all at once and don't bother to change the water halfway through so I can get it finished quickly. As I rush into the hall, Dad hands me the car keys. I'm excited and nervous at the same time as I get into the car. I settle myself down and switch the engine on. Having adjusted the rear-view mirror, I put it in reverse gear. Right, deep breath, let's get out of the drive without taking the other hinge off.

The café double swing doors

The day trippers have gone home, and the cleaners have finished in the café. We can hear the extractor fans in the takeaway and occasionally the boss's voice as he waves and shouts hello to a passer-by. It's the calm before pub closing time when everyone is chucked out on to the pavements. Full of beer, they'll stagger down here and queue for a bag of chips, before wending their way home or returning to the nearby caravan park.

A group of teenage girls is chatting and giggling opposite. Wearing miniskirts not much wider than belts, not much is left to the imagination. They're probably heading to one of the bars opposite the beach. Flashing disco lights and loud music, definitely not my cup of tea. I've just spotted Nina. Out on the town again. She'll be good for nothing tomorrow. Still, who can blame them for having a good time whilst they can. Skegness is dead in the winter. I feel sorry for the waitresses who don't live in town, missing out on all the fun. No buses run at night in these parts. Maybe now the new girl has passed her test, things will be different.

In a couple of hours, after the takeaway shuts its doors, there will be nothing more to look at. The odd stray dog, a police car circling past maybe. Time for some shut eye before those bloody seagulls start up again. Not that we ever get much sleep anyway with that Town Hall clock carrying on all night.

CHAPTER 13

Potato (*Solanum tuberosum*)

1980 AND 2001

'Mum, whilst I am a student, I think it would be criminal not to fit in as many long-haul adventures as is humanly possible.' (Diary entry 2017)

'Let me take a photo of all of you. Look at the size of that rucksack. I can't bear it. He's going for ages, isn't he? Gap year, is it?' (British Airways stewardess at Heathrow international departures 2012)

'So far, I have only done five continents in the world. Need to tick off the other two in the next few years.' (20-year-old son)

She experiences freedom like she has never known before. She has money in her pocket, and no one else to worry about. The Hauptbahnhof (main train station) with connections all over mainland Europe is only twenty minutes by underground from the office. Her weekend adventures are lengthened by a German system of clocking in and clocking out, which means short working hours on Fridays. 'She's having a whale of a time, swanning all over Europe,' Mum tells everyone. Answerable only to herself, she does not realise how precious this combination of financial wherewithal, no responsibilities and freedom to do as she pleases truly is.

Before I set out to Germany, I was nervous. I had never been away from home and family. Other than a couple of days with my friend visiting her aunt, or the occasional school trip. My mum had reassured me I would be fine, 'You're good at making friends, and I'm sure there will be lots of young people working in the same place, keen to make friends. And then there's your badminton. There's bound to be a group somewhere you can join in with. You'll see, it will be fine. It will be time to come back before you know it.' And from my dad, 'I'd have given my eye teeth to do something like that when I was your age. Flying to the moon would have seemed no less probable. I didn't get on a plane until I was forty.'

I cry all the way to Heathrow in the back seat of the car. Nearly thirty years later, I will drop one of my sons at Heathrow and watch him go through departures, knowing he is going to do a volunteer project in one of the most dangerous countries in the world. I swallow back the tears, only this time it is him reassuring me, 'I'll be fine, Mum and Easter will come round quickly.'

My parents exchange glances in the front seats but sit stony faced and listen to the radio. There are no words of comfort and I also feel guilty for being upset. I am fortunate to have landed a job at a publishing house in Stuttgart, thanks to a contact of my parents. I think no further than the end of my nose. It does not occur to me that this opportunity might set me up for a career after I have graduated. The idea that I might use the time I am employed there to build up a network of contacts for the future does not enter my head. I treat it no differently than any other casual holiday job I have had.

I was swept up by the Günther family when I arrived in Germany. I pay them board and lodging, and I share a room with their daughter. She is fifteen, though seems a lot older given her sensible, no nonsense outlook on life. She doesn't mean to be censorial, but I feel frivolous in her presence, and guilty for wanting to travel and have a good time. The family is kind and welcoming and I am treated as one of them.

Frau Günther sweeps across the car park underneath my office window. She is a stout woman with a brown woollen coat, sensible winter shoes and layers of cardigans and overalls. She is carrying one of those creamy yoghurts she knows I like and looks up at the window where I sit and puts her head on one side quizzically whilst pointing to it. She is always worried about my stomach being empty. Which is why I have put on about 3 kilos already in the few weeks since being in Germany.

I nod because I know she will bring it up anyway. I tell my boss I'm just going down to meet Frau Günther. 'More food?' he smiles above his *Time Out* magazine. All the editors at the publishing house where I work seem to spend a lot of time reading news magazines that I have never heard of. One by one, they have invited me out to their apartments at the weekend, where I have met their families and gone for walks in parks or forests.

When I arrived, my German was faltering, and the objective is to improve it before going to Cambridge next year. I can't even think that far forwards. That's a whole different level of worry. Am I clever enough? Was I just lucky to get the 'A' level grades I got? The plane over to Stuttgart was half empty and I distracted myself from thinking about what would happen when I landed by gazing out into the clouds. My first airplane flight. I chatted to another British girl I met whilst queueing for the loo. We swapped seats so we could sit next to each other and carry on talking. She was going to be an au pair for a Rudolf Steiner family in the Black Forest. She told me a bit about what this meant for their way of life and how she would have to fit in. We exchanged telephone numbers and said it would be nice to meet up.

I took a taxi to the security lodge I had been told to report to by the company employing me. There was a nice friendly man there who wasn't expecting me. Turns out it was Herr Günther. He made a couple of telephones calls and then put two and two together and found the keys to the place they had rented for me. He asked me if he could help with my luggage and I followed him down the street to the apartment block.

There was an incredible smell of spices. 'Gastarbeiter,' he said to me. I wasn't sure what this meant. We went up to the 12th floor and he opened the door to my bedsit. It was all coloured grey, just like I was feeling. A sofa bed, a table and chair and a kitchenette plus shower room. He looked at me in a concerned way. I was tearful but managed to say that I needed to telephone my parents to let them know I had arrived ok. We went back to the security lodge and he handed me the phone. I called Mum and Dad who had been waiting anxiously for news. 'Yes, I've arrived OK. Yes, I've seen my flat. It's small but it's fine. It's in a huge block next to a motorway. Opposite a BMW showroom. Yes, a nice man has helped me with my luggage. Yes, I'm a bit tired so need to sleep. Yes, I have still had the picnic tea Mum packed me. I'll put the phone down now as the call is expensive.'

The kind man looked at me. 'Do you know Stuttgart?' he said in German. I shook my head. 'I'll send my daughter over tomorrow. She is 15, and she will show you around the city centre and help you.' A guardian angel.

Heike arrived, a bundle of red hair, big glasses with a strong organised energy at precisely the time he had said. She appraised me. Yes, I looked every bit as lost as her father had probably described to her. I had woken up to the noise of the motorway and felt like an alien who had landed somewhere unknown. 'Kom,' she took me in hand. And we marched purposefully downtown. She showed me the public transport stops and the Hauptbahnhof, the main train station. Stuttgart is a beautiful city, and I was dazed by the busy flow of people rushing about their Saturday morning business. 'Mutti says would you like to come for lunch today.' I said thank you. She showed me where they lived, in the caretaker's second floor apartment just behind the office block where I would be working.

I went to lunch and there was a homely smell that I appreciated properly for the first time in my life. Mutti rushed around in an apron and overwhelmed me with questions and kindness. 'Sit down. Have a drink. I'm cooking a special German lunch for you.' I could see the parents talking together. She came into the room where I was sitting with Heike looking at her English books. 'Would you like to come and live with us? You will pay us the same rent as for the apartment, but you would live with us as a family and share our meals.'

I moved my stuff in and started work at 7.30am the next day. I quickly got into my new routine. My job is to build the index at the back of an English language textbook for German children. It's very relaxed. They call me Jude. People leave on the dot of 5pm and clock out at the main gate. I have never had so much money in my life. After paying my rent, I still have plenty in my bank account.

It's a daily procession of one meal after another. Mutti lays out breakfast for me at 6.30am. She says I mustn't go to work with an empty stomach. Coffee and bread with ham and cheese. Then around 10, me and my boss and the others on our floor all go down to the company restaurant for our 'zweites Frühstück' (second breakfast). Strong coffee and more bread, cheese and ham. Then we all work for a couple of hours before lunch. Piles of pasta and thick Bavarian stew. In the late afternoon, we have Kaffee Kuchen (coffee and cake). I generally manage a walk downtown before Abendessen (evening meal) with the family.

I go to stay with the Rudolf Steiner family in the woods. The house is freezing and there is thick snow on the ground. The house is chaotic. My friend explains that they eat and live according to quite strict rules. No sweet things. No fried foods. Lots of grains and seeds. Raw vegetables by the bucket load. No coffee no alcohol. I think it is a bit joyless. But the Black Forest is stunning. Thick snow, children sledging, adults cross-country skiing.

I sit with Frau G sometimes at night in the sitting room when Heike is doing her homework, her endless homework that she does with such diligence. 'You work hard at school, you go to senior school, you go to technical college or university. You get a good job.' I will never meet a single young German person who thinks differently. It is drilled into them.

The sitting room is toasty warm and has brown corduroy settees and G Plan furniture, the kind that will become very trendy again. It's next to the tiny kitchen where I have my first breakfast every morning. I tell her please I can get my own breakfast because she has much to do before she goes out around 6.30am. But she is adamant. You are paying us rent; therefore, I get your breakfast every morning. She always asks me last thing at night what I would like. I give up arguing with her after a while.

She seems sad to me. She watches romances on television or escapist films, and she cries buckets into her wine glass. She calls it her 'Glasschen' (little glass) of wine, which turns out to be quite a lot. As she becomes more mellow, she tells me the story of her father in the east part of Berlin and how she has not seen him for years. He is old now. She shows me photos of the kindly looking man in his late 70s. He lives by himself after her mother died. She can send letters and parcels, but everything gets censored at the border. Anything nice she sends gets taken by the East German authorities. He sends her letters. She shows them to me. Obviously opened and then resealed, they are full of thick blue lines where words once had been. She only thinks about when she can see him next. She tells me I am a good listener. The first of many times someone will say this to me.

She tells me the same story maybe twice a week. And as she has more wine, she cries. The family all make fun of her tears. 'Oh Mutti, there she goes again. Crying over things she cannot change. How much wine has she had?' But I always remember her pain and when the Berlin wall will fall nine years later, I will think of her and all the families like her. She asks me about my grandparents and tells me I am so lucky to be able to see them whenever I want. Another thing I have always taken for granted.

Frau Günther asks my friend from the Rudolf Steiner family to lunch and sets the table in the tiny dining room because she is a guest. She makes my favourite Wiener Schnitzel and serves it with a huge platter of her famous Kartoffelsalat (potato salad). At first, I found this dish extraordinarily rich. Usually served warm, it is made with white wine vinegar, mustard and olive oil. Lots of onions and garlic. But now, like a lot of German food, I find it comforting, and anyway I have bought a new pair of jeans to accommodate my growing waistline. My friend keeps telling her how good it is because she hasn't had anything like this since arriving at Stuttgart Airport. Frau Günther doesn't hide her disdain for the way her host family is living. After lunch we go downtown and people watch. We go to the Christmas markets and we drink Glühwein. It is magical but freezing cold.

'Kaffeekuchen?' my friend says. She hasn't had anything sweet to eat for months and has been looking longingly into every patisserie window. We find a cosy coffee house and don't stint on our choices. Along come the huge plates of torte with whipped cream. We see an elderly couple watching us and smiling. They are enjoying our delight. Eventually we must go back outside to the now dark late afternoon. We ask the waitress for the bill, slightly fearfully because it is an expensive place. She tells us the elderly couple who have now left, have paid for us as well, saying they wanted to treat us. We don't even get chance to thank them.

To mitigate the vast number of calories, I start to play

badminton. It's up in a sports hall near the Fernsehturm, (the television tower) which is a landmark in the city. I enjoy the weekly outings and it's nice to do something where I don't have to concentrate on speaking German the whole time. I get picked for team matches and am referred to as 'die kleine Englanderin' (the little English girl). I am invited to spend a weekend with the badminton crowd up in a chalet in the mountains. We have to put snow chains on the tyres for the last part of the mountain road and then walk the final few kilometres through thigh deep snow, carrying our provisions for the weekend to the mountain hut which has no heating and basic dormitories. Some go out skiing during the day. Others read or go for walks. I am spellbound by the beauty of the place and gaze out of the tiny hut window out into the mountains. We make big fires, eat Wurst and Sauerkraut (sausages and cabbage) and drink Jägermeister.

At badminton, I meet another friend whom I see most weeks. We go for a beer and Wurst sometimes in the evenings. A trainee optician, she can only afford a tiny bedsit in town on her wages and returns to the family farm at the weekends. Her family is proud she will have a good professional job. Her parents make a modest living but have no complaints. When I visit them, they live very simply and treat me like royalty. I am struck by their pride in their daughter who has worked to escape their hard way of life.

With flexitime, I finish work by 3.00pm on Fridays. With my pre-bought ticket, I rush out of work and head down to the Hauptbahnhof. The departures board reads like the who's who of European cities. Hamburg, Berlin, Paris, Vienna,

Salzburg, Cologne, Prague, Munich, Gerona. I will tick all of these off in my time there. I visit family friends or relatives wherever they are in Europe and explore new places with my newly made friends. I am enjoying being European and love the continental way of life. I love the seamlessness of the travel across borders. I enjoy switching from German to French and then back again. In exactly 40 years' time, the UK will be about to exit the EU and I will think it is one of the saddest things to happen in my lifetime.

When I travel home for Christmas, nothing has changed, but I realise I have. I am no longer that girl from Lincolnshire who is afraid of anything different or new. I can't wait to go back out to Stuttgart to the life I have made there.

In twenty years she gets on a plane to Egypt, leaving her children and her husband behind for the very first time, and she is reminded of that 'Friday afternoon at the Hauptbahnhof' feeling. That freedom to focus on what is ahead of her and not worry about anything else. What luxury. She did not deeply appreciate it when she was in Stuttgart, but she sure does now. Now she has three children, all still of primary school age but not tiny anymore. She has struggled through professional jobs, been successful, but decided it is time to have more space for the family and herself. She has always wanted to visit the Pyramids and she has taken up cycling now she has fewer commitments. When she saw the notice in the paper to take part in a charity cycle ride down the Nile for a women's charity, it called to her. Her first solo big adventure since those train trips in Europe.

She wakes up on the first morning on the small riverboat

that she will spend the next week on with a hundred other women. It was dark when she arrived, so she looks through the window, which is only just above the level of the water, and there's a man alongside the boat in a dugout canoe selling trinkets. Smiling and holding them up to her as she looks out bleary eyed. She smiles back. She has never done anything like this and is nervous about cycling 450km in the heat over five days. But excited. In Cairo she had visited the Pyramids, which her youngest son is learning about at school. Crawling through the tiny pitch-black tunnels inside them is almost more of a challenge than the cycling will be, but she knows it isn't an option to tell her five-year-old she has been unable to do it. She buys him a picture of them to take home for him.

She has travelled all over the world with work. Left the family behind, usually for a day or maybe two. And needed to think ahead to what everyone would need in the short time she was away and tick things off the list. But this is different. There are no clients to please or be concerned with. No seminars she needs to prepare for. No business articles she is required to read to keep up to date. No team members to consider. She had left a simple list of arrangements for the children with her mum, who had said to her, 'Just go and don't worry about anything here. You have deserved this.'

All she has to do is get up, choose which cycling shorts and top to wear and go to the breakfast buffet with her things she needs for the day. And then pedal. Not to have any other responsibility is strange but liberating. And when she has finished cycling for the day, she takes her weary legs back to the cabin and showers, then lies on the bed reading.

Potato (*Solanum tuberosum*)

Something she has forgotten she can do. No one is asking her for anything. No one is needing anything. No one is shouting up the stairs. No one to worry about but herself. Her feelings of guilt quickly vanish.

She loves being amongst a huge crowd of women. Female company has always been important to her. She values the openness of the conversation, the warmth and the empathetic connection. There is nothing quite like the camaraderie, the sisterhood, the humour and belly laughter amongst friends away from the responsibility of work, family and home. All through her adult life she has made time for lunch and coffee dates, book clubs, girls' nights out and mini-breaks with like-minded souls. She feels blessed to have been surrounded by such wonderful women as she has navigated through the ebbs and flows that are life.

Whilst cycling in Egypt, every day brings different cycling companions and new stories. She is captivated by the scenes she passes as she cycles through hidden villages and vast agricultural landscapes. Women sit hunched over by the river, scrubbing and rubbing clothing on boards by the water and then rinsing in the water. Hordes of scantily dressed children play near them, laughing and screaming with delight as they splash each other.

Men carry huge loads balanced on either end of a giant pole across their shoulders. She sees one of them turning around and doesn't appreciate the rotation circle is bigger than she thinks. She is knocked to the ground by one end of the load and surrounded by concerned onlookers as she lies unhurt in the dust in the middle of a remote Egyptian village.

The end of Ramadan, and there is a police escort for the last few kilometres to Luxor. Horns beeping. Two different worlds collide. As the period of fasting finishes, 100 Lycra-clad western ladies cycle through the streets and watch the circles of men who are gathering and sitting in the streets, as they wait for their women folk to serve their food.

She finds the colours of Egypt magical. The Nile is not sludgy grey but the most brilliant azure blue. The desert is yellow like an egg yolk, and the irrigated strip of land which connects the two as bright a green as she has ever seen. It is a beautiful sight. She never forgets those colours and the impact they have on her. She feels like she would like to capture them in a painting or drawing. But she does not have an artistic bone in her body, so she has been told repeatedly over the years, so she buys a sketch made by a local artist and puts it in the bottom of her travel holdall as a keepsake.

CHAPTER 14

Sweetcorn (*Zea mays convar*)

1985

My red Mini Metro won't start again. It's a standing joke with my three housemates, all friends from university. We share an extremely cold 1950's detached house which we rent in Neasden, an exceptionally untrendy backwater in the suburbs, but it's handily on the Jubilee Line. 'NW10 is on the up,' we joke to ourselves, 'we're ahead of the trend.' The rent is £150 per month each including bills, just within our tight budgets. The owner is Persian and has furnished the place with ornate, unrobust items, some of which won't survive our tenancy. Frosted glass-fronted cabinets line the walls of the small kitchen. A set of chrome and leather dining chairs sit underneath the round smoked glass table in the dining room which we will never use, and a white leather three-piece suite and nest of tables with spindly legs adorn the sitting room.

All the radiators have glass shelves over them, which sit on white painted wrought iron frames. Upstairs, there are gold taps, a plum-coloured bathroom suite and white veneer fitted bedroom furniture with faux gold inlay. The headboards on the beds are covered either in cream PVC or red crushed velvet. Net curtains cover the aluminium double-glazed windows. We have covered the items we consider the most offensive with large, brightly coloured Indian cotton bedspreads. Various other textiles imported from holidays abroad are dotted randomly around the place, as are a couple of road traffic signs that we have 'liberated' from the vicinity, believing that they add a touch of student-like quirkiness. We never see our neighbours, unless they have come to complain about the noise we have made or are making.

I have a faulty alternator, the car mechanic said. If it

carries on causing a problem, it needs replacing. I run back into the house and yell upstairs, 'Can you give me a push please?' I hear cries of disbelief. One by one they come downstairs in various stages of undress. 'Again?' they chorus. 'Sorry. I've got to be in Hangar Lane by 8.00am for a burst pipe, otherwise I'd leg it to the tube.'

A well drilled team, they stand in front of the bonnet and push me backwards out of the drive. I manoeuvre the car so it's facing down the hill. Then they line up at the back and, I hear, 'One two three, push.' I turn the key in the ignition as I start to move and there's a splutter, then the engine starts. I wind down the window and shout thanks everyone, not daring to stop in case I can't start it again.

My friend Liz, a structural engineer, and I spend the evenings during the week together but at the weekends go to our respective boyfriends' flats. They each live in squalid places, but they're closer to the action and our other friends. My two male housemates, both trainee accountants, come and go without a predictable pattern, sometimes with 'extras'. Liz complains that their nights of noisy passion keep her awake and about not being able to get into the bathroom with its plum-coloured suite. My bugbear is the pint of milk in the fridge being 'borrowed' and not replaced. When it's just the four of us, we make Harvey Wallbanger cocktails and watch old films. We are not terribly domesticated. Occasionally we drive in my mini to the local Iceland shop to stock up on frozen mince, chicken pieces and pizzas.

It's the coldest winter for twenty years in London. Dollis Hill Park is at the back of the house. We have a long garden and jump over the fence at the end if we want to stroll there. The snow has almost gone now and yesterday it was above freezing for the first time in two weeks. The fax machine at the office barely stopped all day with instructions to go and inspect water damage insurance claims.

Last July I arrived bright-eyed and bushy tailed at the offices in Wembley ready for my first day as a trainee loss adjuster. The job was the only one I was offered, graduating as I did in the middle of a recession, having hand-written over a hundred applications. It takes five years to qualify as a chartered loss adjuster, so more exams involved, which was not in my plan. However, to mitigate this, the job was based in London, which was where all my friends were heading and my boyfriend, and having a good social life was of more significance to me than building a career. Further vindication came when my dad told me he knew someone who was a partner in a loss adjusting firm whom he described as 'loaded, with a great big house in Bramhall and children at Manchester Grammar'.

Getting my Mini Metro in the first place caused a lot of aggro. Its engine size was 0.1 litre larger than the allowance for my grade. The significance was largely lost on me, but it did not go unnoticed with the others in the office, who put it down to blatant favouritism because I was a) a woman and b) a Cambridge graduate. Collecting the damn thing from the Bristol based dealership the firm had an arrangement with was also fraught with complication. I had to get a train there, then drive it back into London.

Trouble was, I had only ever driven in Lincolnshire, and

the route I had memorised from the end of the M4 to Wembley was a distant memory as soon as I hit the traffic of central London. Lost, I went round the Marble Arch roundabout several times, desperately trying to see something, anything to give me a clue where to go. In the end I saw a red double decker bus with Kilburn on it, and I knew that would take me up the A5 in the right direction. So, I followed it, stopping every time it did, finally getting to Wembley two hours later than I should have done.

I can't say I love the work, but it's not boring and no two days are alike. Within the office, there is a group of us who are all in in our twenties. Two of the male trainees, ex-public school rugby playing lads, like to have a laugh and there's a lot of harmless flirting and trying to concoct opportunities for going out for drinks after work. Insurers usually fax across new claims for us to loss adjust, unless they are significant amounts or possible fraud is suspected, in which case one of the partners will be contacted by phone. Sometimes we go out to visit new cases in pairs, and we usually have a bit of a laugh discussing the claims that we think are dodgy, or the other people in the office.

But usually I set out by myself in my Mini Metro with the London *A to Z* open on the passenger seat so I can see it easily, and the stack of green claim files on the back seat that are my calls for the day. Little by little, my geography of North West and Central London is improving, and I enjoy the feeling of the streets becoming more familiar to me. And I have got to meet the full gambit of London life. I have loss adjusted claims for authors, popstars and TV producers and seen inside stunning Georgian properties in Hampstead, four-storey townhouses in Maida Vale and duplex apartments overlooking Regent's Park.

I have also visited tower blocks in Harlesden where the lifts aren't working and there are groups of young men hanging around, looking at me intently as I make my way up the emergency stairs to flats on the floors above. I don't think twice about my discomfort. I just get on with it. My mother would be horrified. I tell her that there is an office mobile phone, a large heavy brick like thing, but I don't tell her that usually someone more senior always gets first dibs on it and I have no way of contacting anyone when I am out and about doing my claims visits.

The senior partner asks me to come into his office and tells me about a conference next week. 'Lots of senior people from the firm will be there. It's at a very swanky hotel in Bayswater and it might be good for you to go along and meet some of them. There is always a nice buffet lunch.' I'm worried this will add to the 'blatant favouritism' narrative, but he is adamant, 'Lesley is going too and will keep an eye out for you and introduce you to people.' I really like Lesley, the only senior woman in the office. She is professional and approachable, and I think it will be nice to spend more time with her. Anyway, it seems I don't have much choice.

We drive to the Connaught Hotel in Bayswater together. Given her seniority, Lesley has a car with a 1.6 litre engine, and I tell her the story about my Mini Metro. 'The boys and their cars. You'll get used to it,' she laughed, 'there's always someone with their nose being pushed out of joint, because they think the car allocation is unfair.' She looks briefly across at me. 'And then you got the desk by the window. Normally you have to be here at least two years before that happens.' It seems there are all sorts of unseen and unspoken of obstacles to trip me up.

We park the car and walk round the side of the hotel. Normally I just pass places like this as I'm driving around and think how posh it looks. We go through the revolving door and make our way to the desk in the atrium, where we are given our badges with a safety pin on the back. Annoyingly, I have a polyester blouse on, so I'm worried the pin will leave a hole in it. It's alright for these blokes wearing jackets, I think. Right, deep breath. We go into the ante room next to the lecture theatre and Lesley suggests we get a coffee. I watch as the room fills up and people introduce themselves to each other. I am terrified about putting a foot wrong or saying something stupid. I feel very underdressed in my blouse and skirt. Note to self, I must get a suit in case I have to come to one of these again.

Roving conference microphones

We get to see the light of day when there is a conference or an event such as a wedding. This looks like it's going to be a dull affair. Lots of men in grey suits. Usually, they choose young ladies to carry us up and down the tiered rows of seats, and their job is to look out for the eager beavers who want to ask questions, usually men. My money is on the two young lovelies I've just spotted coming through the revolving doors into the red carpeted lobby. The younger one looks like a trainee and is unsure of herself. The other woman is a bit older and has a red dress on. Looks more confident and self-assured. Might be a partner.

In the morning there are various talks about actuarial risk and indemnity only policies, very technical and not terribly interesting if I am honest. We are sitting in a large lecture theatre. As I look around, out of three hundred people I can count fewer than a handful of women in total. At coffee break, I notice clusters of men talking earnestly amongst themselves, leaving the women looking helplessly on. I'm standing there feeling like a spare part when Lesley comes over to rescue me and introduces me to some bigwig from the head office, who proceeds to talk to me as if he were my dad. 'How nice to have a lovely young lady trainee in the Wembley team. How are you getting on amongst all those boys?'

At least there's no queue for the ladies' loo. I linger there as long as I dare, feeling the lovely soft hand towels, helping myself to the luxury soap in the dispensers and spraying my wrists with the scent left out on the ledge above the white handbasins. There's even an orchid in here. The bigwig I was introduced to earlier is leading the session after coffee, talking about the firm's exciting future plans. Lots of expansion, more recruitment and greater promotion opportunities for all. Everyone claps loudly at the end.

The buffet lunch is set out at one end of the room. Lots of glass serving dishes with big spoons in them. As I move towards it, there are blokes coming away, serviettes tucked into their shirt collars, with huge platefuls. I wonder if there will be anything left. All that remains is some rice, bits of lettuce, dried bits of fried fish, some kind of stew that presumably once had chunks of meat in it, a few peas and carrots and a huge quantity of sweetcorn. I had some sweetcorn once out of a tin and didn't care for its sickly taste or squeaky texture but needs must. I put a heap on my plate and cover it with the sauce from the stew.

Balancing a plateful of food, a knife and fork and trying to carry a glass of wine at the same time is beyond difficult. Some of the sweetcorn falls onto the purple carpet. It could not stand out more starkly. A waiter makes a great thing of waving a colleague over to come and clear it up. Lesley finds me and we head for a free table at the side of the room. The grey suits mill around. The noise level increases and there's a lot of backslapping and handshaking. I can't be bothered to join the queue for pudding but manage to bag a few After Eight mints served with the coffee. As the final clearing up is taking place, we are approached by the bigwig again.

He has that look on his face that makes you think he is going to ask you a favour, but somehow, he is doing you a favour at the same time. 'Now ladies, time to sing for your supper. We thought how nice it would be if the two of you would be our roving microphone carriers for the afternoon. Nothing much to it. After the keynote talk, the speaker will ask if there are any questions. Just keep your eyes peeled for chaps putting up their hands. When you see someone, whoever is nearest, if you can go over as quickly and quietly as you can with the microphone so we can all hear it loud and clear. Is that alright? Eunice, my secretary, will show you the ropes. Thank you so much.' And then he is gone.

Roving conference microphones

Here we go. The battle axe running the show is approaching. Wouldn't want to meet her alone on a dark night. She is gesturing to the two lovelies I saw earlier to follow her. Here they come. I told you as much. The younger one doesn't look that happy. She's still fiddling with that name badge. She follows the one in the red dress. A few words of explanation and we will be handed over. Our moment of glory. Will have to keep my thoughts to myself from now on. They've switched us on and tested that we're working ok.

And so, we became roving microphone eye candy for the afternoon. Well, that wasn't in the job description.

Up and down the tiered staging we go with the young ladies. You can always predict who's going to ask a question. Nearly always men. Keen as mustard to show everyone how smart they are. First question. 'What impact will computers have on the loss adjusting profession?' Not for me to say mate, but my guess is a lot of you won't have a job in a few years' time, no matter what they said about expansion and all the rest of it. And then, 'How can we attract more women into the profession?' Hilarious. Not by making them carry roving microphones around that's for sure. And this one tops them all, 'How can we ensure loss adjusting is seen as a respectable career like accountancy or the law?' Well maybe start by getting rid of your reputation for reducing everyone's claims, that might help. Finally, the chap at the podium thanks everyone and says there is no more time for questions. The young lovelies hand us back to the battle axe who will return us to the hotel conference team like some no longer wanted present, ready for the next lot. Blimey they were some of the most tedious yet. Like watching paint dry listening to them.

I am still gobsmacked as we drive back to the office. If this is what having a female prime minister does for women in the workplace, god help us. I ask Lesley on the way back to the office how she feels about being demeaned and not taken as seriously as the blokes? She just shrugs her shoulders, 'It's how it is in this firm. And in loss adjusting generally. You have to get on with it. I'm used to it, and you will get used to it too,' she says in a matter-of-fact way.

I plough on through the burst pipes claims. I know all about how to ventilate damp rooms, procure dehumidifiers and get quotes for replastering, redecorating and replacing furniture, fixtures and fittings. I crack on through the workload and study for my exams in the evenings. I earn plaudits for my work rate and for receiving few complaints from claimants. When I tell my dad I'm thinking of applying for new jobs, because 'loss adjusting is not me', he doesn't say so, but I glean he thinks I am being short sighted. After all, it's a good stable job, so why go looking for something else? Although I know what I don't want to do, I don't know what I do want to do. I look on the university jobs list and see a post advertised for a recruitment consultant. I have no idea what one of those is, but think I match the attributes they are looking for. I apply.

Garden behind rented house in Neasden

We'll be pleased to see the back of this lot of tenants. They're the only young people in the road and they've had a couple of very noisy parties. At least this one is in the garden. They're celebrating all four of them passing their first-year exams and the one with the Mini Metro that they push started down the hill has a new job. Their tenancy is up in a few weeks' time and they're all moving on.

The big excitement is we can clearly hear Bob Geldof's Live Aid concert at Wembley a few miles away. It's a hot still evening. All the neighbours are out in their gardens. We can hear the crowds cheering and they're doing an encore of the 'Feed the World' anthem. Some party goers have jumped over the fence into the park for a game of rounders. Others are lying around on the grass. There are empty bottles and cans everywhere.

One of them has made some carrot soup. A strange thing to make on a hot summer's night, but apparently, it's a long-standing tradition. More people travel up the Jubilee Line and arrive, to this place they've heard jokes about and never been to. The music gets turned up. A deputation goes out to the off licence near the big roundabout for more drink. It gets a bit sordid. Someone throws up in a flower bed, and a big chap pulls the radiator and the glass shelf off the wall as he stumbles back against it. At about one in the morning, it's still going strong, until one of the neighbours comes round and complains. There'll be sore heads tomorrow.

I go into work the following Monday. The senior partner calls me in to congratulate me on my exams success and says he's sure I'll qualify in record time. I thank him and then tell him I have got another job and I'm giving in my notice. 'Oh no, he says,' what a shame. 'And to think, you got that bigger engine as well.'

CHAPTER 15

Watercress (*Nasturtium officinale*)

2010 TO 2018

2011

The former occupant of the house was 90 years old, American, and a force to be reckoned with. Over 50 years separated from her husband, a former Director General of Bermuda, she was confined to a cold kitchen, the only habitable room in a dilapidated house in Cumbria. Although an old lady, both her spirit and constitution were strong. She sat by the AGA, the only source of heat in the whole place. In the evenings, she put on an extra pair of socks and covered herself with blankets. She was visited by relatives and village folk, whom she entertained with stories from her carriage driving days and a dram or two. After she died, her four daughters reluctantly put the property on the market. The house felt like part of their family. The estate agents' use of understatement was masterful. 'A rare opportunity to acquire a listed property in a popular North lakes village. The property comes with over an acre of land and several outbuildings which have potential for conversion into holiday accommodation, subject to planning. Some modernisation and updating is required.'

Sketchbook bought from Paperchase

A ceramicist friend has suggested she should buy me. So she can capture anything she sees that speaks to her artistically. She wants to start uncovering her creative side but doesn't know how. Her friend says this will give her some clues. When she was waiting for the train back to Stockport after a long day of meetings, she saw me on the shelf in Paperchase at Euston Station. But that's as much action as I've had. I've been collecting dust on a shelf in her home office for the last two years. Wedged between the little book that contains all her security passwords and a London A to Z. Most likely I've been completely forgotten and will finish up in a packing crate when they move from here. I've heard them talking about it. Quite frankly, life was more interesting at Euston Station. At least there, I could people watch.

2010

We have just sold our long-time holiday house in Cumbria. Until recently, it was an idyllic escape from our lives of busyness. Another world only an hour and forty minutes' drive away up the M6. We discovered that teenagers and rural life don't mix well together and the protests about being removed from the Manchester social scene got stronger and harder to ignore. We had already experienced a frustrated fist go through the plasterboard of a bedroom wall and finally an outburst from our eldest which was the nail in the coffin, 'I'd rather watch paint dry than be up here. It's so boring.' Six months later we reluctantly called in the estate agent who earnt his fee quickly. We put the furniture into storage and I had a last cup of tea sitting on my favourite bench in the garden overlooking the stream. The rooks were calling loudly as if to say, 'don't go'. We pledged that when the boys left home, we would buy another property and return to the area.

We are sitting in the pub in the middle of Greystoke, having viewed a house on the road out of the village which is for sale. It has a view of the castle and a beautiful garden but we both decide its dark interior is not for us. It's cosy in here and the fire is roaring. We forget about housing particulars, savour our beer and allow ourselves to relax in the comfy seats. The local weekly bus from Penrith has just stopped outside and a couple have got off with their shopping and come inside for a warming glass of sherry. We wonder if this is their weekly routine.

We decide to have a bowl of soup and stay a while longer. The friendly landlady we will come to know as Jan, comes over and asks us whether we have had a nice morning. We tell her we are looking to buy a property locally and she points across the road, 'Well if you want a project, there's one over there. I believe it's listed.' We can only see chimney pots above the overgrown hedge. We have cycled past many times and not even realised there is a house behind it. Curiosity gets the better of us and we walk round the perimeter of the hedge after we have finished lunch. That evening at home, we find it on the internet. Shortly thereafter, we make an appointment to view it. 'At least it will be a day out,' Stephen says as if he has already dismissed it as a realistic prospect. 'It looks like it's in a terrible state.'

A couple of Fridays later, we drive to Cumbria. We walk up the path, which in former times would have been just wide enough to allow a carriage to enter, stop outside the front door and discharge its occupants. The estate agent is waiting for us with a giant iron key that he jiggles around to fit inside the lock. Already I start planning, as if we have decided to buy the place, 'That conifer needs taking down. The old gateposts could look great if they were restored. We could grow clematis up the old iron gates that are falling off their hinges at the far end of the drive.' As we enter the dark, damp house,

I wonder if there are ghosts here. The estate agent reads my mind, 'Apparently there is the spirit of a servant girl in the house. She had a relationship with the son of a former owner and when she became pregnant, he was sent away to sea in disgrace. She never stopped hoping he would come back and is still waiting for him.'

It is a forbidding space. I can hear water dripping. Other than that, it is eerily quiet. It has been added to several times over the centuries. Large day rooms with crumbling plaster and peeling wallpaper. Ancient wiring and no heating. Then we duck our heads to move between the dark ground floor rooms, where once the laundry and stores would have been. I'm imagining how I would redesign the space. The kitchen at the front of the house comprises only an ancient AGA, a sink and a cupboard riddled with woodworm. 'This is the part of the house where the old lady lived,' the estate agent apologises, 'hence the rather makeshift shower room. But of course, you can easily make it all into one big space.' I can visualise a huge kitchen with plenty of space for when the family comes back and for social gatherings. After looking at more derelict rooms upstairs 'with massive potential', I am drawn to the garden. From the main bedroom there is a view down to the yew hedge, but I can't see beyond it. I excuse myself, saying I need some fresh air.

It's like an overgrown abandoned secret garden with tangles of plants jostling for position in the overcrowded borders. South facing, it has different 'rooms' within it, separated by yew hedges and gravel pathways. A large, most perfectly shaped Sycamore tree provides some shade from the sun. There is a wonderful ancient oak tree beyond the drive, several of its branches fractured and lying on the ground next to it. A passer-by shouts 'Morning' over the crumbling wall. I wave back overly enthusiastically and then feel a bit ridiculous. I stand there, taking it all in. There is something magical about the place. I imagine the generations of people who have lived here before. Though it is more than 'a bit of a project', I don't feel overwhelmed by it. I am peaceful here. I linger next to what was once probably a herbaceous border and enjoy the moment.

To begin with, I think it's because the idea of ghosts has been put into my head. But I realise it is indeed the ghost of Grandma striding around the garden as though in search of something. I now know we will buy this place and live here. It's a sign. Eyes down, she looks annoyed to be disturbed.

'Eeh, what yer gawping at pet? Ah'm just picturin' mysen in this garden. By gum, yer'd bi' takin' on some project 'ere. D'yer know what yer doin'? It's a bottomless pit thou knows. Mind, it's reight peaceful. After all that strivin' yer've done, it's 'bout time yer 'ad a bit o' a rest. Ah've bi'n ear wigging as folks 'ave bi'n passin' by. They're not like 'em nosey parkers we 'ad at back of bungalow in Cleethorpes. Reckon ah wouldn't bi' mithered 'ere.'

2012

After a few months of legal comings and goings, we complete the purchase. We meet architects and builders and submit plans. 'Think big,' they encouraged us, 'you will probably have to compromise.' In the end, the local authority austerity measures meant one conservation officer for the whole of Cumbria, so they stipulated we had to keep the outside the same, allowing our project for reconfiguring the inside of the house to go ahead. Walls knocked down, giant steel beams put in, the house shell reveals its years of decay. Every two weeks at the site meeting, there's a predictable sequence of events. The builder points out the latest problem, scratches his head and puts forwards possible solutions. Stephen asks, 'How much?' and the provisional sums get added to the financial spreadsheet that runs our lives.

The invoices from the building company land like clockwork at the end of every month. My vague plan to cut back on the number of work commitments disappears as quickly as the funds from our bank account. I feel relief after winning new projects, thereby avoiding financial ruin. But then I get a sinking feeling in my stomach as I imagine the days and weeks in my calendar being blocked out by meetings, early morning and late evening train journeys then writing and presenting reports to senior egos that respond best to validation and praise. I feel overwhelmed by the lack of space that I know will be the reality in the coming weeks.

Sketchbook bought from Paperchase

Still no action to report. Just more dust. Still hanging around on this shelf minding my own business. She's either fretting about that building project or her work. No prospect of me getting a look in any time soon.

I run faster and faster, but my to-do list gets bigger not smaller. The financial pressures are such it has become clear we need to sell our family house in Altrincham to be able to carry on with the renovation work in Cumbria. More stress and hassle, but we're in a hole and we have no choice but to keep digging. I imagine Kevin McCloud from *Grand Designs* descending at any moment to give us a ticking off for failing to keep to budget.

The market is flat, we finally get a buyer, but the sale is complicated. I don't know what to worry about first. Sometimes I wish we had never started the project. Friends have little sympathy. They look at us as if to say, 'Well what did you expect?' We are both exhausted by the worry and certain knowledge that we have only ourselves to blame for our current misfortune.

2014

Sketchbook bought from Paperchase

When she is looking for something else, she finds me and looks inside my cover. Nothing there. She sighs. She takes me down to the kitchen and leaves me on the kitchen table. Well, at least it's a change of scene and there's a lot more comings and goings in here. One day, as she is going out cycling, she picks me up and puts me in her backpack. I really hope she doesn't leave me in here. No view at all. After about an hour along a smooth road, then ten minutes along a much bumpier one, she stops, sits in the sun on the grass verge and takes me out. She is looking across the road at some tall striking orangey scarlet flowers with drooping heads against the backdrop of a green hedge. She takes a couple of felt tip pens, and sketches on the first page. She is relaxed and immersed in her endeavour. After she has finished, she sits quietly. Not something I see her do very often. She pops me back in the bag and gets back on her bike.

Sketching had brought a few brief moments of stillness to my life. Inspired, I surfed the net for creative courses and found an introduction to mosaics in Brighton. It is for 'beginners who love working with colour and textures'. The memory of those amazing colours in Egypt when I cycled down the Nile came back to me very vividly. I felt guilty escaping from everything, but it was the lull before the final storm, and I needed a break and figured being by the sea for a few days would re-energise me. As I boarded the train, I felt a freedom I hadn't done for years. Not since my last charity cycle ride in Tanzania.

It's such a treat having breakfast laid out for me in the homely Bed and Breakfast place where I am staying. Nothing to distract me. I take a walk on the promenade every morning. I breathe in the air and remember why we are moving to Cumbria. The course is so unlike any previous one I have been on. No one is in a hurry. Or stressed. Or constantly looking at their phones. There is a plate of homemade muffins and a jug of fresh lemonade on the kitchen table next to the big room we are all working in which overlooks the sea.

The creative process envelops me. I am surprised where it takes me. Having learnt basic cutting techniques, I am drawn to using the pieces of broken china and ceramics. I start experimenting, mixing clashing colours and different textures. 'Interesting,' is the teacher's verdict. I complete a mirror and abstract picture and feel I have achieved something. I am reminded of the boys running out of school carrying their precious creations as I get off the train and proudly show them to everyone.

2015

Eventually lady luck smiles upon us, the house purchase goes through and we can crack on and finish the renovation project in Cumbria. Now we can start to look forwards and get excited. On our visits, we choose finishes and agree final details. The house feels updated and refurbished yet retains its authenticity and history. New open plan spaces sit alongside the older part of the house, where the footprint is unchanged. As we look ahead, others in the well-ordered suburb that has been our home for twenty-five years feel threatened, 'Don't you like it here?' some ask, as if our impending move is a reflection on their choices, 'Won't the village regard you as incomers?'

Finally, moving day comes along, we leave our rented house that was home for eighteen months and head up the M6. In all, three huge lorries disgorge their contents. The piano is wheeled in on a wooden plank balanced over the low stone wall at the front. Everything else is carried in by the tired looking blokes in overalls. Finally, everything is in its place and I can stop telling the men which room to put things in, ticking the items off my list as they go into the house. As I drive into Penrith to get fish and chips for everyone, I am both relieved and exhausted.

We settle into the house. I am still commuting to London several days a week and, increasingly, I am frustrated when I miss out on glorious fine days because of travel or work. And when I get off the train at Penrith Station after a couple of days away, I breathe in the fresh air and realise how much I have missed it. We have started to make plans for the garden and I can barely wait to get changed out of my work clothes when I get home so I can go and see progress. It's still a muddy mess, but the shape is starting to reveal itself and I pore over plant encyclopaedias and garden magazines for design ideas. I want to plant the herbaceous borders first then start thinking about my vegetable patch. I'm seriously thinking of enrolling on the RHS horticulture course run at the local college.

Sketchbook bought from Paperchase

When she is not in London, she now takes me for her daily circular dog walk. It's been a cold autumn and winter so far, but everyone chats when you meet them. Most are curious about this new person in their midst. She loves the fact they don't give a fig about what job she does. They're interested in her. Nothing more, nothing less. Her sketches are now more abstract than before, almost sculpture like. She draws outlines of mountains, trees that have fallen in the last storm, clusters of farm buildings or cloud formations.

2018

Having agonised for months, if not years, the decision to let go of all the professional striving appears as if from nowhere. I do my final meeting in London, walking through Green Park afterwards to the tube station for the last time as a working woman. It is weird after so many years. I can see Buckingham Palace surrounded by tourists to my left and a few people to my right are sitting in deckchairs enjoying the early spring sunshine. When I next come to London, I will be one of those visitors who hang around in squares or linger on pavements without a thought for others in more of a hurry. I will be able to spend all day visiting friends, having lunch and going to galleries. It feels decadent beyond measure.

A studio comes up nearby and I go to visit it. A small collection of ceramicists, jewellers and artists have workplaces around a courtyard and a café. Their worlds are so different from the one I have inhabited. Everyone is wandering around in bright coloured clothing and big jewellery. There are benches outside where they gather to drink tea, eat their packed lunch and discuss the exhibition or show they are working towards. I enrol on a sculpting course in north-east Scotland and sign a three-year lease for the studio. I take my work suits to the Oxfam shop.

I do my one and only show about eighteen months later, having completed enough torsos and busts to make it worthwhile. All finished in my trademark upcycled china and ceramics. I know my work is like the proverbial Marmite, but most people smile when they look at it. It is light-hearted and fun. I stand somewhat nervously behind my creations as people start to file in. One woman asks me how much one of the female busts is. When I tell her, she looks like I've said something obscene. I start to apologise, 'Well they do take a long time to make, and I have my studio rent to pay, and the materials are costly.' And another woman, close enough for me to touch her, says to her friend, 'These do absolutely nothing for me. I wouldn't have one of these if you paid me,' like I am invisible. Another says to my face, 'Your work is completely bonkers you do realise that?'

I decide the commercial market is not for me, and not to

put myself through such torture again. Commissions only from now on. To remind me of my commitment, when I get home I put my favourite female torso in the middle of the newly planted herbaceous border. I call her Venus. She deserves a special place in my garden. I start to develop more abstract sculptures, carving shapes out of polystyrene. I make pieces comprising several components, threading them onto metal poles sunk into concrete.

The longer days of spring then summer bring a new rhythm. Most mornings we wake to sunlight streaming through the gaps around the wooden shutters where they have shrunk since being restored. I get up and put on a swimming costume then my shorts and T-shirt, grab my towel and walk to the heated open-air swimming pool just over the playing fields. After showering and chatting with new friends, I walk home, dump my wet things and make breakfast. I take it outside and sit on the new patio. The big yew hedge separates the cottage garden we planted last autumn from a wilder area beyond it. I hear the racehorses and the chatter of their riders before I see them over the top of the newly planted hedge. They are heading back to the stables.

After a wet spring, the warm sunshine is making everything grow almost before my very eyes. There are fewer patches of bare earth now that the *Erigeron* and *Creeping Phlox* are spreading and covering the ground. Butterflies and bees crowd around the *Catmint* at the edges of the herbaceous borders. The yellow *Aquilegias* and lime green *Euphorbias* are fading now, and being replaced by the *Geraniums*, *Lupins*, *Knautias* and *Scabiosa*. Everything has its moment in the sun. Even the big blousy peonies will fade after a few weeks, allowing something else to be centre stage. I bend over to see what else is appearing through the soil.

I go inside to pour another cup of coffee then walk across the drive to the place we plan to start the vegetable garden next year. It was rough meadow, but has now been mowed, so I can appreciate the space better. It faces south and has no big trees anywhere near it. I envisage two raised beds to begin with, side by side, with an asparagus bed at the back. Grandad always said you have to keep asparagus separate so it stays weed free and avoids disease. For the main beds, he kept everything in alphabetical order, starting with the beans at the back of the bed: that way everything gets enough light and sun. I see him bending over his spade pointing out what everything is to a little girl who is spellbound. Then I hear *Test Match Special* coming from my dad's shed, and I see him stretching up as he attaches the tops of the runner bean plants to the wigwams of bamboo canes.

I take my empty cup back to the house and pause near the back door. I am experimenting with growing some herbs and salad crops in terracotta pots and survey their progress every day. It's a comforting ritual that makes me feel glad to be alive. I bend over the pot of watercress which has grown again since I gave it a good dousing of water yesterday and the day before, sufficient to cut a couple of hands full. I take my secateurs from the utility room just inside the back door and pick some of the lovely green leaves and taste their pepperiness, and then harvest some rocket and chives from neighbouring pots. As I take the haul back inside to wash it, I think what I can make with it. Perhaps a watercress and chive quiche served with a salad.

I go back outside and hover by the herbaceous border where the mosaic torso of Venus is, my secateurs poised for further action. The riot of colour around her is reflected in the mirror fragments on her breasts and chest and blends with the pretty flowered china pieces on her back and trunk. I feel a warm wave of contentment in my stomach and chest. I look at the blue sky and I hear another string of horses trotting past. The man at the front puts his hand to his riding hat as if to salute me. 'Another lovely day in paradise,' he shouts. This very spot is where I encountered the ghost of Grandma, the day we saw the house for the first time. I haven't seen her since, but I sense she is never far away. I smile at the memory. And I swear Venus is smiling back at me.